The Supporters' Guide

to

Welsh Football Grounds

2006

EDITOR

John Robinson

Tenth Edition

CONTENTS

British Library Cataloguing in Publication Data
A catalogue record for this book is available from the British Library

ISBN 1-86223-131-1

Copyright © 2005, SOCCER BOOKS LIMITED (01472 696226)
72 St. Peter's Avenue, Cleethorpes, N.E. Lincolnshire, DN35 8HU, England
Web site   http://www.soccer-books.co.uk
e-mail   info@soccer-books.co.uk

Printed by The Cromwell Press

FOREWORD

We wish to thank Bob Budd (cover artwork), Michael Robinson (page layouts), Dave Collins (Welsh Football Magazine), Gareth Davies (Wales International statistics), Ken Tucker (Welsh Football League), Alan Foulkes (Cymru Alliance) and, of course, to the many club officials for their assistance in the compilation of this guide.

We endeavour to provide up-to-date ground photographs whenever possible and welcome contributions from any readers who are able to provide alternatives for use in future issues.

Finally, we would like to wish our readers a happy and safe spectating season and, on page 112 and the back cover of this book, list the various other Supporters' Guides which we publish all of which are priced £6.99 and can be purchased post free from the address opposite.

John Robinson
EDITOR

THE MILLENNIUM STADIUM

Re-Opened: 1999
(Formerly known as Cardiff Arms Park)
Address: Millennium Stadium, Westgate Street,
Cardiff   CF10 1JA
Ticket Office: (08705) 582582

Stadium Tours: (029) 2082-2228
Tours run from 10.00am to 6.00pm daily (until
5.00pm on Sundays)
Pitch Size: 110 × 72 yards
Seating Capacity: 72,500
Web site: www.cardiff-stadium.co.uk

GENERAL INFORMATION

Car Parking: City Centre Car Parks
Coach Parking: Sophia Gardens
Nearest Railway Station: Cardiff Central (5-10 minutes walk)
Nearest Bus Station: Next to Railway Station
Nearest Police Station: Cardiff Centre
Police Telephone Nº: (029) 2022-2111

DISABLED INFORMATION

Disabled Sections: L4 – L14 and along the End touchlines
Disabled Toilets: Situated by the Disabled Areas
The Blind: Headsets with commentaries available
Bookings: Please phone in advance

ADMISSION INFO (2005/2006 PRICES)

Prices vary from game to game
Stadium Tours: Adults £5.00, Concessions £3.00,
Children ages 5-16 years £2.50, Under-5s free of charge

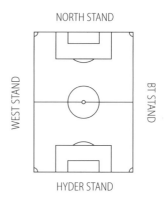

NORTH STAND

WEST STAND

BT STAND

HYDER STAND

Travelling Supporters' Information:
Routes: By Car: Exit the M4 at Junction 29 and take the A48(M) following signs for Cardiff City Centre (via A470). Use the City Centre Public Car Parks; From Cardiff Central Railway Station: Proceed past the Bus Station, cross Wood Street and turn down Westgate Street (alongside the back of the Royal Hotel).

CARDIFF CITY FC

Founded: 1899 (**Entered League**: 1920)
Former Names: Riverside FC (1899-1910)
Nickname: 'Bluebirds'
Ground: Ninian Park, Sloper Road, Cardiff   CF11 8SX
Record Attendance: 62,634 (17/10/59)
Ground Capacity: 21,432
Seating Capacity: 12,908
Pitch Size: 110 × 75 yards

Colours: Royal Blue shirts with Royal Blue shorts
Telephone Nº: (029) 2022-1001
Home Support Ticket Office: (0845) 345-1400
Away Support Ticket Office: (0845) 345-1405
Fax Number: (029) 2034-1148
Web Site: www.cardiffcityfc.co.uk

GENERAL INFORMATION

Car Parking: Leckwith Stadium car park and Street Parking
Coach Parking: Leckwith Stadium car park (adjacent)
Nearest Railway Station: Cardiff Central (1 mile)
Nearest Bus Station: Cardiff Central
Club Shop: At the ground
Opening Times: Weekdays from 9.00am to 5.00pm and Matchdays 10.00am to 3.00pm
Telephone Nº: (0845) 345-1485
Postal Sales: Yes (Internet Sales also accepted)
Police Telephone Nº: (029) 2022-2111

GROUND INFORMATION

Away Supporters' Entrances & Sections:
Grange End Visitors section entrances and accommodation (both standing and seating). Use turnstiles at Entrance F

ADMISSION INFO (2005/2006 PRICES)

Adult Standing: £15.00 – £20.00
Adult Seating: £18.00 – £26.00
Child Standing: £10.00 – £14.00
Child Seating: £8.00 – £21.00
Note: Tickets are cheaper if purchased before the matchday
Programme Price: £2.50

DISABLED INFORMATION

Wheelchairs: 25 spaces available for Home fans, 3 spaces for Away fans in the disabled section, Canton End Family Enclosure
Helpers: One helper admitted per disabled fan
Prices: Disabled children – £8.00; Disabled adults – £18.00; Disabled OAPs – £10.00; Helpers – £10.00
Disabled Toilets: Yes
Contact: (0845) 345-1405 (Away fans must book in advance)

Travelling Supporters' Information:
Routes: From All Parts: Exit M4 at Junction 33 and follow Penarth (A4232) signs. After 6 miles, take the B4267 to Ninian Park.

SWANSEA CITY FC

Founded: 1900 (**Entered League**: 1920)
Former Name: Swansea Town FC (1900-1970)
Nickname: 'Swans'
Ground: New Stadium, Landore, Swansea SA1 2FA
Ground Capacity: 20,000 (All seats)
Record Attendance: 32,796 (at the Vetch Field)
Pitch Size: 115 × 74 yards

Colours: White shirts and shorts with Black trim
Telephone Nº: (01792) 616600
Ticket Office: (08700) 400004
Fax Number: (01792) 616606
Web Site: www.swanseacity.net

GENERAL INFORMATION

Car Parking: Reserved parking only at the stadium but 3,000 spaces are available in a Park & Ride scheme just off Junction 45 of the M4.
Coach Parking: By Police direction
Nearest Railway Station: Swansea High Street (4 miles)
Nearest Bus Station: Quadrant Depot (3 miles)
Club Shop: At the ground
Opening Times: Weekdays 10.00am – 4.30pm and Matchdays 9.30am – 5.00pm
Telephone Nº: (01792) 616600
Police Telephone Nº: (01792) 456999

GROUND INFORMATION

Away Supporters' Entrances & Sections:
North Stand

ADMISSION INFO (2005/2006 PRICES)

Adult Seating: £13.00 – £18.00
Child Seating: £7.00 – £10.00
Senior Citizen Seating: £10.00 – £13.00
Note: Special prices are available in the Family Stand and ticket prices vary depending on the category of the game
Programme Price: £2.50

DISABLED INFORMATION

Wheelchairs: 250 spaces available in total for Home and Away fans together with 250 spaces for helpers
Helpers: One helper admitted per wheelchair
Prices: Normal prices apply for the disabled. Free for helpers
Disabled Toilets: Available
There are 62 disabled parking spaces available at the stadium
Contact: (01792) 616600   (Bookings are necessary)

Travelling Supporters' Information:
Routes: From All Parts: Exit the M4 at Junction 45 and follow signs for Swansea (A4067). The stadium is clearly signposted.

WREXHAM AFC

Founded: 1872 (**Entered League**: 1921)
Nickname: 'Red Dragons'
Ground: Racecourse Ground, Mold Road, Wrexham,
North Wales   LL11 2AH
Ground Capacity: 15,500
Seating Capacity: 10,500
Record Attendance: 34,445 (26/1/57)

Pitch Size: 111 × 71 yards
Colours: Red shirts with White shorts
Telephone Nº: (01978) 262129
Ticket Office: (01978) 366388
Fax Number: (01978) 357821
Web Site: www.wrexhamafc.co.uk

GENERAL INFORMATION

Car Parking: Town car parks are nearby and also Newi
College (Mold End)
Coach Parking: By Police direction
Nearest Railway Station: Wrexham General (adjacent)
Nearest Bus Station: Wrexham (King Street)
Club Shop: At the ground, under the Sainsbury Stand
Opening Times: Office hours only
Telephone Nº: (01978) 352536
Police Telephone Nº: (01978) 290222

GROUND INFORMATION

Away Supporters' Entrances & Sections:
Turnstiles 36-42 for the Eric Roberts (Builders) Stand

ADMISSION INFO (2005/2006 PRICES)

Adult Standing: £14.00
Adult Seating: £14.00 – £16.00
Child Standing/Seating: £5.00
Senior Citizen Standing: £7.00
Senior Citizen Seating: £10.00
Programme Price: £2.50

DISABLED INFORMATION

Wheelchairs: 35 spaces in the Pryce Griffiths Stand
Helpers: One helper admitted per wheelchair
Prices: Normal prices for the disabled. Free for helpers
Disabled Toilets: Available in the disabled section
Contact: (01978) 351332 (Tony Millington) (Please book)

Travelling Supporters' Information:
Routes: From the North and West: Take the A483 and the Wrexham bypass to the junction with the A541. Branch left at the roundabout and follow Wrexham signs into Mold Road; From the East: Take the A525 or A534 into Wrexham then follow the A541 signs into Mold Road; From the South: Take the the M6, then the M54 and follow the A5 and A483 to the Wrexham bypass and the junction with the A541. Branch right at the roundabout and follow signs for the Town Centre.

COLWYN BAY FC

Founded: 1885
Former Names: None
Nickname: 'Bay' 'Seagulls'
Ground: Llanelian Road, Old Colwyn, Colwyn Bay, LL29 8UN
Record Attendance: 2,500

Colours: Sky Blue shirts and shorts
Telephone Nº: (01492) 514581
Fax Number: (01492) 514581
Pitch Size: 112 × 70 yards
Ground Capacity: 3,000
Seating Capacity: 260
Web site: www.colwynbayfc.co.uk

GENERAL INFORMATION
Supporters Club: M. Mottram, 340 Abergele Road, Old Colwyn, Colwyn Bay
Telephone Nº: (01492) 515951
Car Parking: At the ground
Coach Parking: At the ground
Nearest Railway Station: Colwyn Bay (1 mile)
Nearest Bus Station: Colwyn Bay
Club Shop: At the ground
Opening Times: Matchdays only
E-mail: cbfc.merchandise@v21.me.uk
Police Telephone Nº: (01492) 517171

GROUND INFORMATION
Away Supporters' Entrances & Sections:
No usual segregation

ADMISSION INFO (2005/2006 PRICES)
Adult Standing: £6.00
Adult Seating: £6.00
Senior Citizen Standing: £3.00
Senior Citizen Seating: £3.00
Child Standing: £1.00
Child Seating: £1.00
Programme Price: £1.30

DISABLED INFORMATION
Wheelchairs: Accommodated in Covered Terrace
Helpers: Admitted
Prices: Please phone the club for information
Disabled Toilets: Available in the Social Club
Contact: (01492) 514581 (Bookings are not necessary)

Travelling Supporters' Information:
Routes: From Queensferry: Take the A55 and when the expressway is reached take Junction 22 (signposted Old Colwyn). Turn left at the bottom of the slip road then straight on at the mini-roundabout into Llanelian Road. The ground is ½ mile on the right.

MERTHYR TYDFIL FC

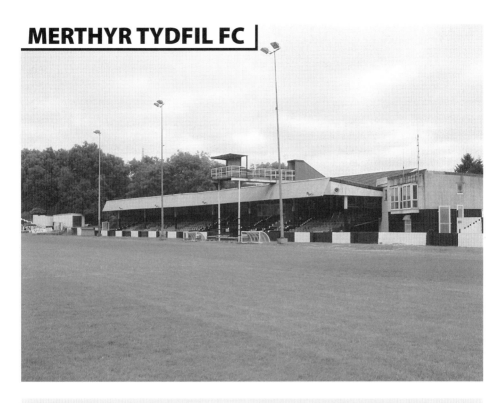

Founded: 1945
Former Names: Merthyr Town FC
Nickname: 'Martyrs'
Ground: Penydarren Park, Merthyr Tydfil, Mid Glamorgan   CF47 8RF
Record Attendance: 21,000 (1949)
Pitch Size: 110 × 72 yards

Colours: Black and White striped shirts, White shorts
Telephone Nº: (01685) 384102
Fax Number: (01685) 382882
Ground Capacity: 6,000
Seating Capacity: 1,500
Web Site: www.themartyrs.com

GENERAL INFORMATION

Supporters Club: Richard Bennett, c/o Club
Telephone Nº: (01685) 384102
Car Parking: At the ground and street parking
Coach Parking: Georgetown
Nearest Railway Station: Merthyr Tydfil (½ mile)
Nearest Bus Station: Merthyr Tydfil
Club Shop: At the ground
Opening Times: Weekdays 9.00am to 4.00pm and Matchdays
Telephone Nº: (01685) 384102
Police Telephone Nº: (01685) 722541

GROUND INFORMATION

Away Supporters' Entrances & Sections:
Theatre End entrances and accommodation

ADMISSION INFO (2005/2006 PRICES)

Adult Standing: £6.00
Adult Seating: £7.00
Under-14s Standing: Free of charge
Under-14s Seating: £1.00
Senior Citizens Standing: £4.00
Senior Citizens Seating: £5.00
Programme Price: £1.50

DISABLED INFORMATION

Wheelchairs: 20 spaces are available in total in front of the Main Grandstand
Helpers: Please phone the club for information
Prices: Please phone the club for information
Disabled Toilets: Available at the Strikers Club (Clubhouse)
Contact: (01685) 384102   (Bookings are not necessary)

Travelling Supporters' Information:
Routes: From the East: Take the A470 to Merthyr. At the top of Merthyr High Street, take a sharp left at the lights and then 1st right into Brecon Road. Take the 1st right and then 1st right once again and follow the road into the ground; From the North: Leave the A465 Heads of the Valleys road for Dowlais. After approximately 2 miles, fork right into Brecon Road. Take the 1st right then 1st right once again and follow the road into the ground.

NEWPORT COUNTY FC

Founded: 1989
Former Names: Newport AFC
Nickname: 'The Exiles'
Ground: Newport Stadium, Stadium Way, Newport International Sports Village, Newport NP19 4PT
Record Attendance: 4,300 (31st March 2004)
Pitch Size: 112 × 72 yards

Colours: Amber shirts with Black shorts
Telephone N°: (01633) 662262
Fax Number: (01633) 666107
Ground Capacity: 4,300
Seating Capacity: 1,200
Web site: www.newport-county.co.uk

GENERAL INFORMATION

Supporters Club: Bob Herrin, c/o Club
Telephone N°: (01633) 274440
Car Parking: Space for 500 cars at the ground
Coach Parking: At the ground
Nearest Railway Station: Newport
Nearest Bus Station: Newport
Club Shop: At the ground
Opening Times: Matchdays only
Telephone N°: (01633) 662262
Police Telephone N°: (01633) 244999

GROUND INFORMATION

Away Supporters' Entrances & Sections:
No segregation unless specifically required by Police

ADMISSION INFO (2005/2006 PRICES)

Adult Standing: £8.00
Adult Seating: £8.00
Senior Citizen Standing: £5.50
Senior Citizen Seating: £5.50
Juniors: £1.00
Programme Price: £2.00

DISABLED INFORMATION

Wheelchairs: Accommodated
Helpers: Admitted
Prices: Normal prices for the disabled. Free for helpers
Disabled Toilets: Yes
Contact: (01633) 662262 (Bookings are not necessary)

Travelling Supporters' Information:
Routes: Exit the M4 at Junction 24 and take the exit at the roundabout, signposted 'Southern Distributor Road'. Go straight on at the first two roundabouts then turn left at the 3rd roundabout. Carry straight on over the next two roundabouts, pass the Velodrome then turn left between the two Carcraft buildings. Take the 1st turning on the left into the Stadium car park.

THE WELSH PREMIER LEAGUE

Address

Plymouth Chambers, 3 Westgate Street,
Cardiff   CF10   1DP

Contact   John Deakin

Phone (029) 2037-2325   **Fax** (029) 2034-3961

Clubs for the 2005/2006 Season

ABERYSTWYTH TOWN FC

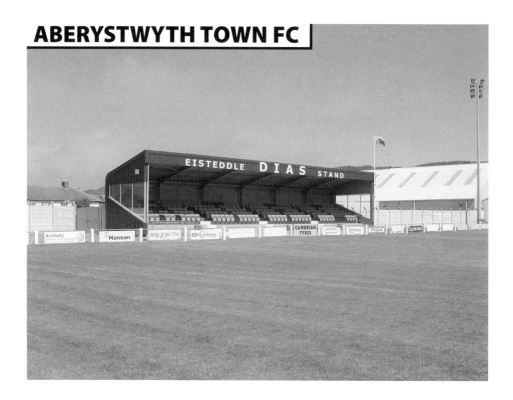

Founded: 1884
Former Names: Aberystwyth FC
Nickname: 'Seasiders'
Ground: Park Avenue, Aberystwyth, Dyfed
Ground Telephone N°: (01970) 612122/617939

Colours: Green and Black shirts with White shorts
Correspondence Address: Rhun Owens, 31 Maes Gogerddan, Aberystwyth
Contact N°: (01970) 623520 or (07773) 230894
Fax Number: (01970) 617939
Web site: www.atfcnews.co.uk

GENERAL INFORMATION
Club Shop: Yes
Car Parking: Adjacent to the ground
Coach Parking: At the ground
Nearest Railway Station: Aberystwyth (¼ mile)
Nearest Bus Station: Aberystwyth (¼ mile)
Nearest Police Station: Aberystwyth
Police Telephone N°: (01970) 612791

GROUND INFORMATION
Ground Capacity: 4,050
Seating Capacity: 550
Record Attendance: 4,000
Pitch Size: 110 x 78 yards

ADMISSION INFO (2005/2006 PRICES)
Adult Standing: £5.00
Adult Seating: £5.00
Child Standing: £2.00
Child Seating: £2.00
Note: Under 14's are admitted free of charge
Concessionary Standing: £2.00
Concessionary Seating: £2.00
Programme Price: £1.00

DISABLED SUPPORTERS INFORMATION
Wheelchairs: Accommodated in the Dias Stand
Disabled Toilets: Yes
Contact Number: (01970) 617939

Travelling Supporters' Information:
Routes: From the Railway Station: Turn left into Park Avenue then right after Greenfield Street and the ground is at the far end on the right behind the Bus Depot; From the East of Town: Follow the 'Town Centre' signs from the Safeway roundabout. The ground is on the left after the Kwiksave store.

AIRBUS UK FC

Founded: 1946
Former Names: British Aerospace FC
Nickname: 'Planemakers'
Ground: Airfield Sports & Social Club, BAE System Airbus UK, Broughton, Chester   CH4 0DR
Ground Phone Nº: (01244) 528317 (Matchdays) (01244) 522253 (Weekday working hours)

Club Colours: Dark Blue shirts and shorts
Correspondence: Mick Mayfield, 8 Meadow Road, Broughton, Flintshire   CH4 0RG
Contact Telephone Nº: (01244) 537107
Fax Number: None
Web site: www.sportnetwork.net/main/s356.htm

GENERAL INFORMATION
Club Shop: At the ground
Car Parking: By the Main Gates
Coach Parking: By the Main Gates
Nearest Railway Station: Shotton (5 miles)
Nearest Bus Station: Chester (5 miles)
Nearest Police Station: Hawarden
Police Telephone Nº: –

GROUND INFORMATION
Ground Capacity: 1,000
Seating Capacity: 250
Record Attendance: 435
Pitch Size: 110 x 75 yards

ADMISSION INFO (2005/2006 PRICES)
Adult Standing: £5.00
Adult Seating: £5.00
Child/Senior Citizen Standing: £2.00
Child/Senior Citizen Seating: £2.00
Programme Price: £1.00

DISABLED SUPPORTERS INFORMATION
Wheelchairs: Accommodated in the Main Stand
Disabled Toilets: Available in Main Pavilion
Contact Number: (01244) 522393

Travelling Supporters' Information:
Routes: Exit the A55 Expressway at the Broughton turn-off and follow signs for the Aerospace Factory. Park at the Main Gates where directions to the ground will be given.

BANGOR CITY FC

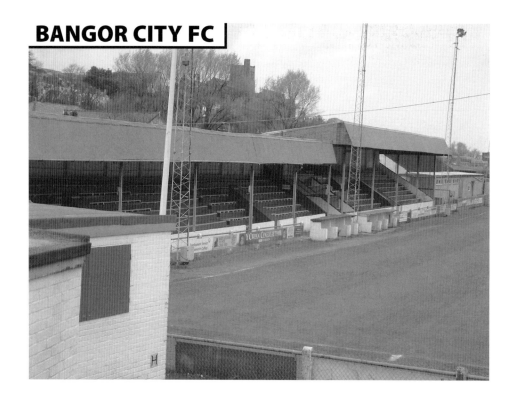

Founded: 1876
Former Names: Bangor Athletic FC
Nickname: 'Citizens'
Ground: The Stadium, Farrar Road, Bangor, Gwynedd
Ground Telephone N°: (01248) 355852

Club Colours: Blue shirts with White shorts
Correspondence Address: Alun Griffiths, 12 Lon Y Bryn, Menai Bridge, Anglesey, Gwynedd, LL55 5NM
Contact Telephone N°: (01248) 712820
Fax Number: (01248) 372132

GENERAL INFORMATION

Club Shop: Yes
Car Parking: Street parking and limited space at the ground
Coach Parking: By Police direction
Nearest Railway Station: Bangor (150 yards)
Nearest Bus Station: Bangor (500 yards)
Nearest Police Station: Bangor
Police Telephone N°: (01248) 370333

GROUND INFORMATION

Ground Capacity: 1,000
Seating Capacity: 700
Record Attendance: 10,000 vs Wrexham – Welsh Cup Final 1978-79
Pitch Size: 118 x 75 yards

ADMISSION INFO (2005/2006 PRICES)

Adult Standing: £6.00
Adult Seating: £6.00
Child Standing: £1.00
Child Seating: £1.00
Concessionary Standing: £3.00
Concessionary Seating: £3.00
Programme Price: £1.00

DISABLED SUPPORTERS INFORMATION

Wheelchairs: Accommodated
Disabled Toilets: None
Contact Number: (01248) 355852

Web Site: www.bangorcityfc.com
E-mail: bangorcity@excite.co.uk

Travelling Supporters' Information:
Routes: Take the A55 Expressway to the A5 turnoff (signposted Betws-y-Coed/Bangor) and follow signs for Llandegai/Bangor. After 2½ miles pass the marina on the right and follow the road to the left. Continue for ¾ mile and the Ground is situated on Farrar Road, 150 yards from Bangor Railway Station.

CAERNARFON TOWN FC

Founded: 1876

Former Names: Caernarfon Athletic FC, Caernarfon Ironopolis FC and Caernarfon United FC

Nickname: 'The Canaries'

Ground: The Oval, Marcus Street, Caernarfon, Gwynedd

Ground Telephone Nº: (01286) 675002

Club Colours: Yellow shirts, Green shorts

Correspondence Address: Ian Sixsmith, Caernarfon Air Park, Dynas Dinlle, Caernarfon   LL54 5TP

Contact Telephone Nº: (0870) 7541500

Fax Number: (0870) 7541510

Web site: www.caernarfontown.net

GENERAL INFORMATION

Club Shop: Yes – at the ground

Car Parking: At the ground

Coach Parking: At the ground

Nearest Railway Station: Bangor (9 miles)

Nearest Bus Station: Caernarfon (½ mile)

Nearest Police Station: Maesincla, Caernarfon

Police Telephone Nº: (01286) 673333

GROUND INFORMATION

Ground Capacity: 3,678

Seating Capacity: 252

Record Attendance: 6,000 vs Bangor City (25/12/26)

Pitch Size: 110 x 70 yards

ADMISSION INFO (2005/2006 PRICES)

Adult Standing: £5.00

Adult Seating: £5.00

Child Standing: £3.00

Child Seating: £3.00

Programme Price: £1.00

DISABLED SUPPORTERS INFORMATION

Wheelchairs: Accommodated

Disabled Toilets: None

Contact Number: (01286) 675002

Travelling Supporters' Information:

Routes: From Bangor: Travel along the A55 coast road. Ignore an "up hill" slip road which has a secondary Caernarfon sign-post on a white background. Exit at a "down hill" slip road further along, signposted Caernarfon A487. Continue on the A487 into Caernarfon and staying on the A487 travel along a short flyover. At the end of the flyover, with the Eagles Hotel facing, move to the left hand lane and follow the A4085 Beddgelert Road. Travel along the A4085 almost to the brow of the hill then turn right into Segontium Road South just before the Roman Fort. The ground is facing at the bottom of the road.

CAERSWS FC

Founded: 1878
Former Names: Caersws Amateurs FC
Nickname: 'Bluebirds'
Ground: Recreation Ground, Caersws, Powys
Ground Telephone Nº: (01686) 688753

Club Colours: Blue shirts with White shorts
Correspondence: Wynne Jones, Arfryn, Trefeglwys, Caersws, Powys SY17 5QY
Contact Telephone Nº: (01686) 430617
Fax Number: (01686) 430617

GENERAL INFORMATION
Club Shop: At the ground (Matchdays only)
Car Parking: At the ground
Coach Parking: At the ground
Nearest Railway Station: Caersws (¼ mile)
Nearest Bus Station: Caersws
Nearest Police Station: Newtown
Police Telephone Nº: (01686) 625704

GROUND INFORMATION
Ground Capacity: 3,000
Seating Capacity: 250
Record Attendance: 2,656
Pitch Size: 110 x 70 yards

ADMISSION INFO (2005/2006 PRICES)
Adult Standing/Seating: £5.00
Senior Citizen Standing/Seating: £3.00
Junior Standing/Seating: £1.00
Programme Price: £1.00

DISABLED SUPPORTERS INFORMATION
Wheelchairs: Accommodated
Disabled Toilets: Available
Contact Number: (01686) 688753

Web Site: www.caersws-fc.com

Travelling Supporters' Information:
Routes: The entrance to the ground is by the River Bridge in Caersws. Caersws is situated on the A470 between Newtown and Llanidloes.

CARMARTHEN TOWN FC

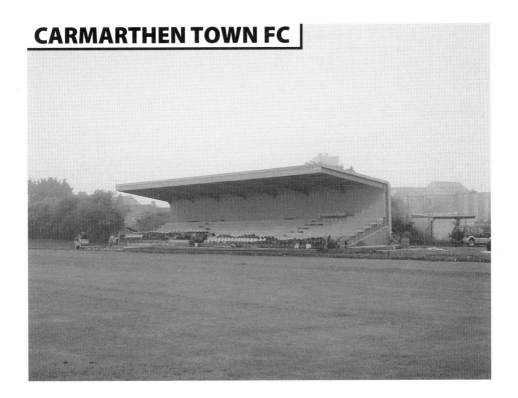

Founded: 1953
Former Names: None
Nickname: 'Town'
Ground: Richmond Park, Priory Street, Carmarthen, Carmarthenshire
Club Office Nº: (01267) 222851

Clubhouse Nº: (01267) 232101
Club Colours: Old Gold shirts and shorts
Correspondence Address: G.O.Jones, Carmarthen Town, 131 Priory Street, Carmarthen   SA31 1LR
Contact Telephone Nº: (01267) 233359
Fax Number: (01267) 222851

GENERAL INFORMATION

Club Shop: Yes – at the ground
Car Parking: Adjacent to the ground
Coach Parking: Adjacent to the ground
Nearest Railway Station: Carmarthen (1 mile)
Nearest Bus Station: Blue Street, Carmarthen
Nearest Police Station: Carmarthen
Police Telephone Nº: (01267) 232000

GROUND INFORMATION

Ground Capacity: 2,000
Seating Capacity: 500
Record Attendance: 3,000
Pitch Size: 110 x 70 yards

ADMISSION INFO (2005/2006 PRICES)

Adult Standing: £5.00
Adult Seating: £5.00
Concessionary Standing: £3.00
Concessionary Seating: £3.00
Note: Children under 12 are admitted free of charge
Programme Price: £1.00

DISABLED SUPPORTERS INFORMATION

Wheelchairs: Accommodated
Disabled Toilets: None – but adapted toilet available
Contact Number: (01267) 232101

Web Site: www.carmarthentownafc.net
E-mail: info@carmarthentownafc.net

Travelling Supporters' Information:
Routes: Proceed into Carmarthen on the A48. Pick up the A40 to Llandeilo at the first roundabout and follow the Town Centre sign at the next roundabout. The ground is situated on the left hand side in Priory Street, behind the Toyota Garage.

CONNAH'S QUAY NOMADS FC

Founded: 1946
Former Names: Connah's Quay Juniors FC
Nickname: 'Westenders'
Ground: Deeside College, Kelsterton Road, Connah's Quay, Flintshire   CH5 4LU
Ground Telephone Nº: (01244) 816418

Club Colours: White shirts with Black shorts
Correspondence Address: R.Hunter, 40 Brookdale Avenue, Connah's Quay   CH5 4LU
Contact Telephone Nº: (01244) 831212
Fax Number: (01244) 831212
Web site: www.nomadsfc.wales.com

GENERAL INFORMATION

Club Shop: Yes
Car Parking: Parking available at the College
Coach Parking: At the ground
Nearest Railway Station: Shotton (1 mile)
Nearest Bus Station: Flint (2 miles)
Nearest Police Station: Wepre Drive, Connah's Quay
Police Telephone Nº: (01244) 814444

GROUND INFORMATION

Ground Capacity: 3,000
Seating Capacity: 500
Record Attendance: Approximately 850
Pitch Size: 110 x 70 yards

ADMISSION INFO (2005/2006 PRICES)

Adult Standing: £5.00
Adult Seating: £5.00
Child Standing: £1.50
Child Seating: £1.50
Concessionary Standing: £1.50
Concessionary Seating: £1.50
Programme Price: £1.00

DISABLED SUPPORTERS INFORMATION

Wheelchairs: Accommodated
Disabled Toilets: Available
Contact Number: (01244) 816418

Travelling Supporters' Information:
Routes: The ground is situated on the main A548 road through Connah's Quay in the grounds of Deeside College.

CWMBRAN TOWN FC

Founded: 1950
Former Names: None
Nickname: 'The Crows'
Ground: Cwmbran Stadium, Henllys Way, Cwmbran, Gwent
Ground Telephone Nº: (01633) 627100

Club Colours: Dark Blue shirts and shorts
Correspondence: I.Greaney, 14 Beechleigh Close, Greenmeadow, Cwmbran, Torfaen NP44 5EF
Contact Telephone Nº: (01633) 877802
Fax Number: None

GENERAL INFORMATION

Social Club Telephone Nº: (01633) 483282
Club Shop: Yes
Car Parking: At the ground
Coach Parking: At the ground
Nearest Railway Station: Cwmbran (2 miles)
Nearest Bus Station: Cwmbran (1 mile)
Nearest Police Station: Cwmbran (1 mile)
Police Telephone Nº: (01633) 838999

GROUND INFORMATION

Ground Capacity: 8,201
Seating Capacity: 3,000
Record Attendance: 8,148 vs Manchester United (1994)
Pitch Size: 112 x 76 yards

ADMISSION INFO (2005/2006 PRICES)

Adult Standing: £6.00
Adult Seating: £6.00
Child Standing: £2.00
Child Seating: £2.00
Concessionary Standing: £2.00
Concessionary Seating: £2.00
Programme Price: £1.00

DISABLED SUPPORTERS INFORMATION

Wheelchairs: Accommodated
Disabled Toilets: Available
Contact Number: (01633) 627100

Web Site: www.cwmbrantownafc.org
E-mail: ian@igreaney.wanadoo.co.uk

Travelling Supporters' Information:
Routes: From All Parts: Take the M4, exit at Junction 26 and follow signs for Cwmbran. At the first roundabout (approximately 1½ to 2 miles) take the first exit. Proceed along Cwmbran Drive passing the Stadium on your right. At the next roundabout take the first exit and at the following roundabout take the 3rd exit. The Stadium entrance is 150 yards on the right.
On foot from the station – proceed to the dual carriageway, turn left and Henllys Way is on the right after 1 mile.

GRANGE HARLEQUINS FC

Founded: 1935
Former Names: Grange Juniors FC
Nickname: 'The Quins'
Ground: Cardiff Athletic Stadium, Leckwith, Cardiff
Ground Tel. Nº: (029) 2022-5345

Colours: Red shirts with White shorts
Correspondence: Ian Phillips, 13 Glyn Eiddew, Pentwyn CF23 7BP
Contact Tel. Nº: (029) 2021-6407
Fax Number: (029) 2021-6407

GENERAL INFORMATION
Car Parking: 1,600 space car park next to the ground
Coach Parking: Space for 30 coaches next to the ground
Nearest Railway Station: Grangetown
Nearest Bus Station: Cardiff Central
Nearest Police Station: Canton
Police Telephone Nº: (029) 2022-2111

GROUND INFORMATION
Ground Capacity: 5,000
Seating Capacity: 2,500
Record Attendance: 1,219 vs Cwmbran Town (Welsh Cup)
Pitch Size: 110 x 76 yards

ADMISSION INFO (2005/2006 PRICES)
Adult Standing: £5.00
Adult Seating: £5.00
Concessionary Standing: £3.00
Concessionary Seating: £3.00
Child Standing: £2.00
Child Seating: £2.00
Programme Price: £1.00

DISABLED SUPPORTERS INFORMATION
Wheelchairs: Accommodated – Lift access in Grandstand
Disabled Toilets: Available
Contact Number: (029) 2022-5345

Travelling Supporters' Information:
Routes: Exit the M4 at Junction 33 and take the 1st exit (Leckwith Interchange) signposted for "Athletics Stadium and Leckwith Industrial Estate". Take the 1st exit at the next roundabout onto the B4267 (Leckwith Road). The Stadium us situated on the right after 200 yards.

HAVERFORDWEST COUNTY FC

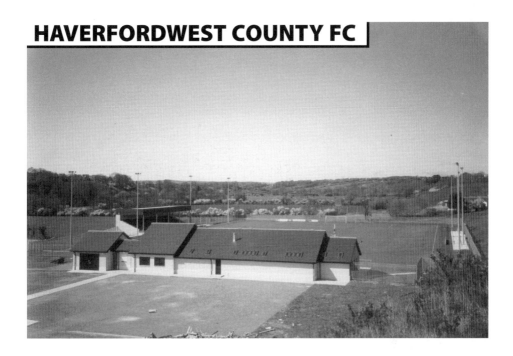

Founded: 1899
Former Names: None
Nickname: 'The Bluebirds'
Ground: The Bridge Meadow Stadium,
Haverfordwest, Pembrokeshire   SA61 2EX
Ground Telephone Nº: (01437) 769048

Club Colours: Blue shirts and shorts
Correspondence Address: c/o Club
Contact Telephone Nº: (01437) 731779
Fax Number: (01437) 769048
Web Site: www.haverfordwestcounty.com
E-mail: barry.vaughan@tesco.net

GENERAL INFORMATION

Social Club Telephone Nº: (01437) 769048
Club Shop: Yes – at the ground
Car Parking: At the ground
Coach Parking: At the ground
Nearest Railway Station: Haverfordwest (½ mile)
Nearest Bus Station: Haverfordwest
Nearest Police Station: Haverfordwest
Police Telephone Nº: (01437) 763355

GROUND INFORMATION

Ground Capacity: 2,500
Seating Capacity: 400
Record Attendance: 2,416
Pitch Size: 110 x 75 yards

ADMISSION INFO (2005/2006 PRICES)

Adult Standing: £6.00
Adult Seating: £6.00
Under-16s Standing: £2.00   (Under-5s admitted free)
Under-16s Seating: £2.00   (Under-5s admitted free)
Concessionary Standing: £4.00
Concessionary Seating: £4.00
Note: Junior Bluebirds club members are admitted for free
Programme Price: £1.00

DISABLED SUPPORTERS INFORMATION

Wheelchairs: Accommodated
Disabled Toilets: Available
Contact Number: (01437) 731779

Travelling Supporters' Information:
Routes: Take the A40 to Haverfordwest and into the Town Centre. Pass the Railway Station, take the 4th exit at the roundabout and the take the 1st exit at the next roundabout. At the following roundabout, take the 'Safeways' exit and turn left alongside Safeways Supermarket. The ground is situated at the end of the road.

LLANELLI FC

Founded: 1896
Former Names: None
Nickname: 'Reds'
Ground: Stebonheath Park, Llanelli, Dyfed
Ground Telephone Nº: (01554) 772973

Club Colours: Red shirts and shorts
Correspondence Address: Nigel Evans,
16 Tyshia Road, Llanelli SA15 1RW
Contact Telephone Nº: (01554) 776760
Fax Number: (01554) 758018

GENERAL INFORMATION
Club Shop: None
Car Parking: At the ground
Coach Parking: At the ground
Nearest Railway Station: Llanelli (2 miles)
Nearest Bus Station: Llanelli (1 mile)
Nearest Police Station: Llanelli (1 mile)
Police Telephone Nº: (01554) 772222

GROUND INFORMATION
Ground Capacity: 3,700
Seating Capacity: 700
Record Attendance: 18,000 vs Bristol Rovers
Pitch Size: 114 x 73 yards

ADMISSION INFO (2005/2006 PRICES)
Adult Standing/Seating: £5.00
Child Standing/Seating: £3.00
Concessionary Standing/Seating: £3.00
Programme Price: £1.00

DISABLED SUPPORTERS INFORMATION
Wheelchairs: Accommodated
Disabled Toilets: Available
Contact Number: (01554) 772973

Web Site: www.llanelliafc.co.uk
E-mail: hugh@hughroberts.wanadoo.co.uk

Travelling Supporters' Information:
Routes: Take the M4 to Junction 48 and exit onto the A4138. Go straight on over three roundabouts and enter Llanelli, turn right at the traffic lights then left after a short distance into Penallt Road for the ground; From the Station: Travel along Station Road to the Town Centre then turn right into Murray Street then into Stepney Place and James Street before turning right into Alban Road. Turn left into Bradford Street and then right into Evans Terrace for the ground.

NEWI CEFN DRUIDS FC

Founded: 1869 then re-named Druids in 1872. The current club was formed in 1992 with the amalgamation of Cefn Albion FC and Druids United FC
Former Names: Plasmadoc FC, Druids United FC, Cefn Druids FC, Flexsys Cefn Druids FC
Nickname: 'The Ancients'
Ground: Plaskynaston Lane, Cefn Mawr, Wrexham, LL14 3AT

Ground Telephone Nº: (01978) 824279
Colours: Black & White striped shirts, Black shorts
Correspondence Address: c/o Club
Contact Telephone Nº: (01978) 824332
Fax Number: (01978) 824332
Web Site: www.cefndruids.co.uk

GENERAL INFORMATION

Club Shop: At the ground
Car Parking: At the ground
Coach Parking: At the ground
Nearest Railway Station: Wrexham
Nearest Bus Station: Wrexham
Nearest Police Station: Ruabon
Police Telephone Nº: (01978) 290222

GROUND INFORMATION

Ground Capacity: 2,000
Seating Capacity: 300
Record Attendance: 602
Pitch Size: 110 x 72 yards

ADMISSION INFO (2005/2006 PRICES)

Adult Standing: £5.00
Adult Seating: £5.00
Child Standing: £1.00
Child Seating: £1.00
Concessionary Standing: £1.00
Concessionary Seating: £1.00
Programme Price: £1.00

DISABLED SUPPORTERS INFORMATION

Wheelchairs: Accommodated
Disabled Toilets: Available
Contact Number: (01978) 824279

Travelling Supporters' Information:
Routes: From All Parts: Take the A483 and Wrexham Bypass then take the A539 towards Llangollen. After 200 yards turn left towards Rhosmedre on the B5605. After 1 mile turn right at the Plough Inn towards Cefn Mawr and after the Kwiksave supermarket turn left down the narrow lane to the ground.

23

NEWTOWN AFC

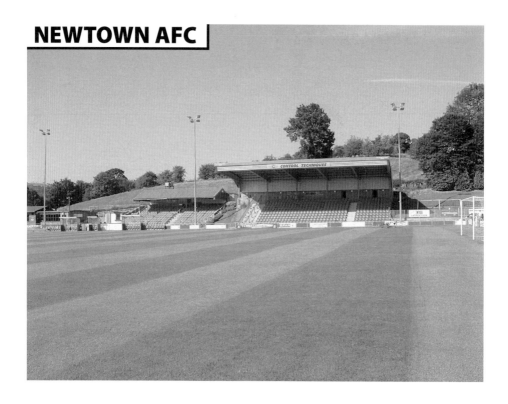

Founded: 1875
Former Names: Newtown Whitestars FC
Nickname: 'The Robins'
Ground: G.F. Grigg Latham Park, Newtown, Powys, SY16 1EN
Ground Telephone Nº: (01686) 623120
Social Club Telephone Nº: (01686) 626159

Club Colours: Red shirts and shorts
Correspondence: c/o Club
Contact Telephone Nº: (01686) 623120 or 626159
Fax Number: (01686) 623120
Web Site: www.newtownafc.co.uk
E-mail: office@newtownafc.co.uk

GENERAL INFORMATION

Club Shop: Yes – at the ground
Car Parking: At the ground
Coach Parking: At the ground
Nearest Railway Station: Newtown
Nearest Bus Station: Newtown Back Lane
Nearest Police Station: Newtown
Police Telephone Nº: (01686) 625704

GROUND INFORMATION

Ground Capacity: 4,999
Seating Capacity: 1,280
Record Attendance: 5,004 vs Swansea (1955)
Pitch Size: 112 x 72 yards

ADMISSION INFO (2005/2006 PRICES)

Adult Seating: £6.00
Child Seating: £3.00
Concessionary Seating: £3.00
Programme Price: £1.00

DISABLED SUPPORTERS INFORMATION

Wheelchairs: Accommodated
Disabled Toilets: Available
Contact Number: (01686) 623120

Travelling Supporters' Information:
Routes: The ground is situated on the fringe of the Town Centre, just next to the junction of the A483 and A489 behind the Police Station. Turn into Park Lane from Park Street by the Town Library. Latham Park is 400 yards along Park Lane on the left.

PORTHMADOG FC

Founded: 1884
Former Names: None
Nickname: 'Port'
Ground: Y Traeth, Porthmadog, Gwynedd
Ground Telephone N°: (01766) 514687

Club Colours: Red & Black striped shirts, Black shorts
Correspondence: D.G. Owen, 56 Maes Gerddi,
Porthmadog LL49 9LE
Contact Telephone N°: (01766) 512991
Fax Number: (01766) 513053
Web site: www.geocities.com/port_fc/

GENERAL INFORMATION

Club Shop: Yes – at the ground
Car Parking: At the ground
Coach Parking: At the ground
Nearest Railway Station: Porthmadog (½ mile)
Nearest Bus Station: Porthmadog (½ mile)
Nearest Police Station: Porthmadog
Police Telephone N°: (01766) 512226

GROUND INFORMATION

Ground Capacity: 4,000
Seating Capacity: 500
Record Attendance: 3,500
Pitch Size: 116 x 76 yards

ADMISSION INFO (2005/2006 PRICES)

Adult Standing: £6.00 (£5.00 for members)
Adult Seating: £6.00 (£5.00 for members)
Child Standing: £2.50 (Accompanied by an adult only)
Child Seating: £2.50 (Accompanied by an adult only)
Senior Citizen Standing: £3.00 (£2.50 for members)
Senior Citizen Seating: £3.00 (£2.50 for members)
Programme Price: £1.00

DISABLED SUPPORTERS INFORMATION

Wheelchairs: Accommodated
Disabled Toilets: Available
Contact Number: (01766) 514687

Travelling Supporters' Information:
Routes: At the crossroads in the town (by Woolworths), go down Snowdon Street, cross over Madog Street and pass the British Legion Club and Porthmadog Pottery Workshop. Carry on over the railway crossing and the ground is situated on the right; Alternative Route: Turn at the side of the British Rail and West Highland Railway Stations into Cambrian Terrace and continue for ½ mile then turn at the fish and chip shop past the Porthmadog Pottery. Then as above.

PORT TALBOT TOWN FC

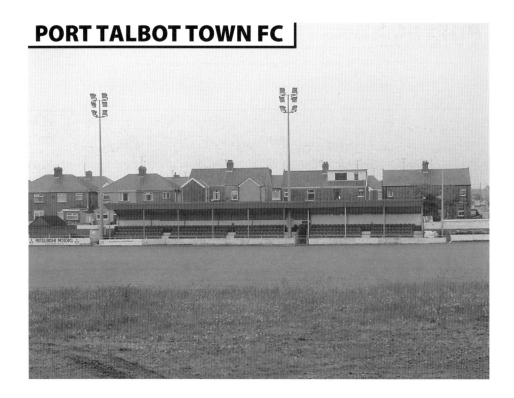

Founded: 1901
Former Names: Port Talbot Athletic FC
Nickname: 'The Blues'
Ground: Victoria Road Ground, Victoria Road, Port Talbot   SA12 6AD
Ground Telephone Nº: (01639) 882465

Colours: Blue shirts and shorts
Correspondence: John Dawkins, 37 Berrylands, Port Talbot   SA12 6LQ
Contact Telephone Nº: (01639) 791172
Fax Number: (01639) 886991
Web Site: www.porttalbotafc.co.uk
E-mail: paul@porttalbotafc.co.uk

GENERAL INFORMATION
Social Club Telephone Nº: (01639) 882465
Club Shop: Yes
Car Parking: Street parking
Coach Parking: At the ground
Nearest Railway Station: Port Talbot Parkway (2 miles)
Nearest Bus Station: Port Talbot Centre
Nearest Police Station: Station Road, Port Talbot
Police Telephone Nº: (01639) 883101

GROUND INFORMATION
Ground Capacity: 780
Seating Capacity: 280
Record Attendance: Over 2,000
Pitch Size: 118 x 70 yards

ADMISSION INFO (2005/2006 PRICES)
Adult Standing: £4.00
Adult Seating: £4.00
Child Standing: £2.00
Child Seating: £2.00
Concessionary Standing: £2.00
Concessionary Seating: £2.00
Programme Price: £1.00

DISABLED SUPPORTERS INFORMATION
Wheelchairs: Accommodated
Disabled Toilets: Available in the Clubhouse
Contact Number: (01639) 882465

Travelling Supporters' Information:
Routes: Exit the M4 at Junction 40 and head for the Town Centre. Bear left at the first roundabout for Aberavon beach and turn right at the traffic lights at the Health Centre into Victoria Road. Turn 2nd left after the traffic lights for the ground.

RHYL FC

Founded: 1870
Former Names: Rhyl Skull & Crossbones FC and Rhyl Athletic FC
Nickname: 'Lilywhites'
Ground: Belle Vue, Grange Road, Rhyl, Flintshire
Ground Telephone Nº: (01745) 338327

Club Colours: White shirts with Black shorts
Correspondence Address: Dennis McNamee, 3 Maes Rhoslyn, Rhuddlan   LL18 2YW
Contact Telephone Nº: (01745) 591287
Fax Number: (01745) 338327
Web Site: www.rhylfc.com
E-mail: admin@rhylfc.com

GENERAL INFORMATION
Club Shop: Yes – at the ground
Car Parking: At the ground
Coach Parking: At the ground
Nearest Railway Station: Rhyl
Nearest Bus Station: Rhyl Town Centre
Nearest Police Station: Rhyl
Police Telephone Nº: (01745) 343898

GROUND INFORMATION
Ground Capacity: 3,800
Seating Capacity: 1,000
Record Attendance: 10,000 vs Cardiff City (1952/53)
Pitch Size: 110 x 75 yards

ADMISSION INFO (2005/2006 PRICES)
Adult Standing: £6.00
Adult Seating: £6.00
Child Standing: £1.00
Child Seating: £1.00
Concessionary Standing: £4.00
Concessionary Seating: £4.00
Programme Price: £1.00

DISABLED SUPPORTERS INFORMATION
Wheelchairs: Accommodated
Disabled Toilets: Available
Contact Number: (01745) 338327

Travelling Supporters' Information:
Routes: Take the A55 Expressway and exit at the St. Asaph/Rhyl turn-off. Take the A525 to Rhuddlan. At the roundabout, take the second turning for Rhyl, turn left at the next roundabout and then travel straight on at the next two roundabouts. At the Shell garage, situated about a mile from the last roundabout, turn right along Pendyffryn Road and then left at the junction. The ground is 300 yards on the left.

TOTAL NETWORK SOLUTIONS FC

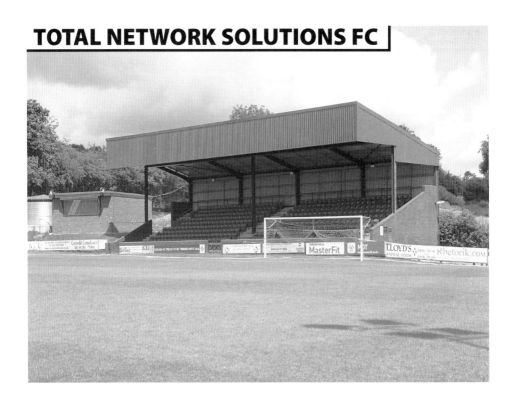

Founded: 1959
Former Names: Llansantffraid FC
The club amalgamated with Oswestry Town in 2003.
Nickname: 'Saints'
Ground: Recreation Ground, Treflan, Llansantffraid, Powys
Ground Telephone Nº: (01691) 828112

Club Colours: Green and white Hooped shirts with White shorts *or* Royal Blue shirts and shorts
Correspondence Address: G.Hughes, Birchlea, Porthywaen, Oswestry SY10 8LY
Contact Telephone/Fax Nº: (01691) 828645
Web Site: www.tnsfc.co.uk
E-mail: ian.williams@tns.co.uk

GENERAL INFORMATION
Club Shop: At the ground
Car Parking: At the ground
Coach Parking: At the ground
Nearest Railway Station: Gobowen & Welshpool
Nearest Bus Station: Oswestry
Nearest Police Station: Llanfyllin
Police Telephone Nº: (01691) 648222

GROUND INFORMATION
Ground Capacity: 2,000
Seating Capacity: 500
Record Attendance: Approximately 2,000
Pitch Size: 110 x 75 yards

ADMISSION INFO (2005/2006 PRICES)
Adult Standing: £5.00
Adult Seating: £5.00
Child Standing: £1.00
Child Seating: £1.00
Senior Citizen Standing: £3.00
Senior Citizen Seating: £3.00
Programme Price: £2.00

DISABLED SUPPORTERS INFORMATION
Wheelchairs: Accommodated
Disabled Toilets: Available
Contact Number: (01691) 828645

Travelling Supporters' Information:
Routes: From the South: Take the B4393 off the A483 Welshpool to Oswestry Road at 'Four Crosses' and head into Llansantffraid. The ground is situated in the centre of the village opposite Wynnstay Farmers Mill. Turn right and the ground is along the road next to the Community Hall; From the North: Take the A483 from Oswestry and turn right onto the A495 at Llynclys. Follow the road to Llansantffraid then as from the South.

WELSHPOOL TOWN FC

Founded: 1878
Former Names: None
Nickname: 'Lilywhites'
Ground: Maesydre, Welshpool, Powys
Ground Telephone Nº: (01938) 553473

Club Colours: White shirts with Black shorts
Correspondence Address: Sarah Hughes, c/o Club
Contact Telephone Nº: (01686) 668176
Fax Number: (01686) 668176
Web site: www.welshpooltownfc.co.uk

GENERAL INFORMATION
Club Shop: None
Car Parking: At the ground
Coach Parking: At the ground
Nearest Railway Station: Welshpool (2 minutes walk)
Nearest Bus Station: Welshpool (5 minutes walk)
Nearest Police Station: Welshpool
Police Telephone Nº: (01938) 552345

GROUND INFORMATION
Ground Capacity: 1,500
Seating Capacity: 250
Record Attendance: Not known
Pitch Size: 108 x 72 yards

ADMISSION INFO (2005/2006 PRICES)
Adult Standing: £5.00
Adult Seating: £5.00
Child Standing: £3.00
Child Seating: £3.00
Concessionary Standing: £3.00
Concessionary Seating: £3.00
Programme Price: £1.00

DISABLED SUPPORTERS INFORMATION
Wheelchairs: Accommodated
Disabled Toilets: None
Contact Number: (01938) 554444

Travelling Supporters' Information:
Routes: The ground is situated on the south side of Welshpool Town Centre. Follow the signs for the Railway Station and turn right just before the station into Howell Drive. The ground is along the lane next to the Junior School.

CYMRU ALLIANCE FOOTBALL LEAGUE

Address

J. Alun Foulkes, 9 Brynteg Estate, Llandegfan, Menai Bridge, Ynys Mon   LL59 5TY

Phone (01248) 713501   **Fax** (01248) 714644

Clubs for the 2005/2006 Season

BALA TOWN FC

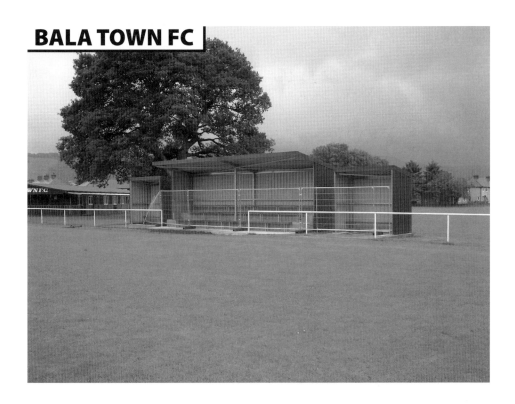

Founded: 1921
Former Names: None
Nickname: None
Ground: Maes Tegid, Castle Street, Bala, N.Wales
Colours: Black & White striped shirts, Black shorts

Correspondence: Nigel Aykroyd, Unit 17, Bala Enterprise Park, Bala LL23 7NJ
Contact Tel. Nº: (01678) 520348
Fax Nº: (01678) 520843
Web Site: None

GENERAL INFORMATION
Car Parking: At the ground
Coach Parking: At the ground
Nearest Railway Station: Wrexham (38 miles)
Nearest Bus Station: Bala

GROUND INFORMATION
Ground Capacity: 1,000
Seating Capacity: 70
Record Attendance: Approximately 500 (during 1946)
Pitch Size: 110 x 70 yards

ADMISSION INFO (2005/2006 PRICES)
Adult Standing: £3.00
Adult Seating: £3.00
Senior Citizen Standing: £1.50
Senior Citizen Seating: £1.50
Junior Standing: Free of charge
Junior Seating: Free of charge
Programme Price: Included with entrance fee

DISABLED SUPPORTERS INFORMATION
Wheelchairs: Accommodated
Helpers: Admitted
Prices: Free of charge for the disabled
Disabled Toilets: Available
Contact Number: (01678) 520348

Travelling Supporters' Information:
Routes: Take the A494 to Bala and turn off the high street by the side of The White Lion into Heol y Castell (Castle Street). The ground is situated on the left hand side after approximately ¼ mile.

BODEDERN FC

Founded: Early 1930s
Former Names: None
Nickname: 'Boded'
Ground: Cae'r Ysgol, Bodedern Secondary School, Bodedern, Anglesey
Clubhouse Tel. Nº: (01407) 740604

Colours: Blue and White shirts with Blue shorts
Correspondence: Richard Jones, 6 Llys Yr Engan, Bodedern, Anglesey LL65 3SX
Contact Tel. Nº: (01407) 742593
Fax Number: –
Web site: www.bodedernfc.com

GENERAL INFORMATION
Club Shop: None
Car Parking: At the ground
Coach Parking: At the ground
Nearest Railway Station: Valley (2 miles)
Nearest Bus Station: Valley
Nearest Police Station: Valley

GROUND INFORMATION
Ground Capacity: 1,000
Seating Capacity: 100
Record Attendance: Approximately 250
Pitch Size: 110 x 70 yards

ADMISSION INFO (2005/2006 PRICES)
Adult Standing/Seating: £3.00
Senior Citizen Child Standing/Seating: £1.50
Programme Price: £1.00

DISABLED SUPPORTERS INFORMATION
Wheelchairs: Accommodated
Disabled Toilets: Available
Contact Number: (01407) 742693

Travelling Supporters' Information:
Routes: From all Parts: Take the A55 Expressway to the RAF Valley turnoff at Junction 4 then follow the signs north to Bodedern. The ground is situated on the left behind the Secondary School as you enter the village.

BUCKLEY TOWN FC

Founded: 1948
Former Names: Fomed by the amalgamation of Buckley Wanderers FC and Buckley Rovers FC in 1978
Nickname: 'Wanderers'
Ground: Globe Way, Liverpool Road, Buckley, Flintshire
Ground Tel. Nº: (07803) 137523

Club Colours: Red and White shirts with Red shorts
Correspondence: Michael Williams, 4 Hillary Grove, Buckley, Flintshire
Contact Telephone Nº: (01244) 546893
Fax Number: None
Web site: www.buckleytownfc.com

GENERAL INFORMATION
Club Shop: None
Car Parking: At the ground
Coach Parking: At the ground
Nearest Railway Station: Buckley (1 mile)
Nearest Bus Station: Buckley
Nearest Police Station: Buckley
Police Telephone Nº: –

GROUND INFORMATION
Ground Capacity: 1,000
Seating Capacity: 80
Record Attendance: Approximately 750
Pitch Size: 120 x 85 yards

ADMISSION INFO (2005/2006 PRICES)
Adult Standing: £3.00
Adult Seating: £3.00
Child Standing: £1.00
Child Seating: £1.00
Programme Price: £1.00

DISABLED SUPPORTERS INFORMATION
Wheelchairs: Accommodated
Disabled Toilets: Available
Contact Number: (01244) 546893

Travelling Supporters' Information:
Routes: Exit the A55 Expressway at its junction with the A550 following signs for Buckley. Pass through Ewloe village and head towards Buckley. As the road reaches the outskirts of Buckley (about 300 yards from Ewloe) turn left at the Red Lion Public House into Globe Way and the ground is about ¼ mile on the right.

FLINT TOWN UNITED FC

Founded: 1886
Former Names: Flint Town FC and Flint FC
Nickname: 'Silkmen'
Ground: Cae-y-Castell, Marsh Lane, Flint, Flintshire
Ground Telephone N°: (01352) 730982
Colours: Black and White shirts with Black shorts

Correspondence Address: A.Baines,
43 Third Avenue, Flint   CH6 5LT
Contact Telephone N°: (01352) 711968
Fax Number: None

GENERAL INFORMATION

Social Club Telephone N°: (01352) 732804
Club Shop: Yes – at the ground
Car Parking: At the ground
Coach Parking: At the ground
Nearest Railway Station: Flint (500 yards)
Nearest Bus Station: Flint
Nearest Police Station: Flint
Police Telephone N°: (01352) 732222

GROUND INFORMATION

Ground Capacity: 3,000
Seating Capacity: 270
Record Attendance: 1,500 vs Wrexham (1994)
Pitch Size: 110 x 75 yards

ADMISSION INFO (2005/2006 PRICES)

Adult Standing: £3.50
Adult Seating: £3.50
Child Standing: £1.00
Child Seating: £1.00
Concessionary Standing: £1.00
Concessionary Seating: £1.00
Programme Price: £1.00

DISABLED SUPPORTERS INFORMATION

Wheelchairs: Accommodated
Disabled Toilets: Available
Contact Number: (01352) 730982

Travelling Supporters' Information:
Routes: Take the A458 from Connah's Quay into Flint then turn right opposite the Swan Hotel into Castle Street following the signs for the Castle. Cross over the railway and the Clubhouse is next to the Lifeguard Station. The ground is along the shoreline opposite the Castle; Alternatively: Take the A55 Expressway and turn off at the Flint sign (A5119) following the road into the town. Turn right at the bottom of the High Street and then left opposite the Swan Hotel over the railway for the Clubhouse and ground.

GLANTRAETH FC

Founded: 1984
Former Names: Llangefni/Glantraeth FC
Nickname: None
Ground: Trefdraeth, Bodorgan, Anglesey
Ground Telephone Nº: (01407) 840401
Club Colours: Red shirts and shorts

Correspondence Address: John Owen, Gallt Ysw, Bethel, Bodorgan LL62 5NL
Contact Telephone Nº: (01407) 840179
Fax Number: None

GENERAL INFORMATION

Club Shop: None
Car Parking: At the ground
Coach Parking: At the ground
Nearest Railway Station: Bodorgan (2 miles)
Nearest Bus Station: Llangefni (6 miles)
Nearest Police Station: Llangefni (6 miles)
Police Telephone Nº: (01248) 722222

GROUND INFORMATION

Ground Capacity: 1,500
Seating Capacity: 75
Record Attendance: Not known
Pitch Size: 110 x 72 yards

ADMISSION INFO (2005/2006 PRICES)

Adult Standing: £2.50
Adult Seating: £2.50
Child Standing: £1.25
Child Seating: £1.25
Programme Price: Included in the admission price

DISABLED SUPPORTERS INFORMATION

Wheelchairs: Accommodated
Disabled Toilets: None
Contact Number: (01407) 840401

Travelling Supporters' Information:
Routes: Exit the A55 Expressway at the Llangefni turnoff and take the A5 signposted for Mona at the roundabout. After about ¾ mile take the B4422 signposted for Aberffraw. Follow this road for 3 miles then turn left at the village of Bethel following the sign for the Glantraeth Restaurant. The ground is situated 1 mile along this road on the right-hand side.

GRESFORD ATHLETIC FC

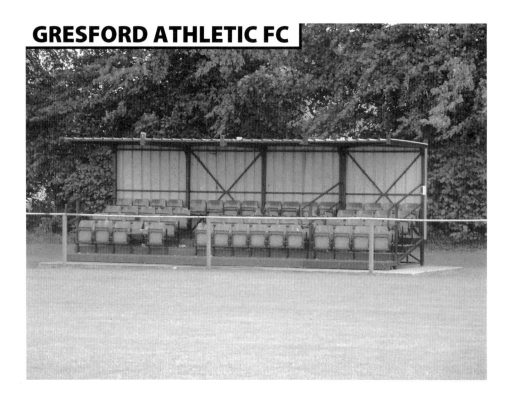

Founded: 1946
Former Names: None
Nickname: 'Athletic'
Ground: Clappers Lane, Gresford, Wrexham
Ground Telephone Nº: None
Web Site: www.gresfordathletic.co.uk
E-mail: chas@gresfordathletic.co.uk

Colours: Shirts are Red with Black and White trim, Black shorts and Red socks
Correspondence: D.C.Rowland, 26 Gorse Crescent, Marford, Near Wrexham, LL12 8LZ
Contact Telephone Nº: (01978) 855354
Fax Number: (01978) 855354

GENERAL INFORMATION

Club Shop: None
Car Parking: At the ground
Coach Parking: At the ground
Nearest Railway Station: Wrexham (4 miles)
Nearest Bus Station: Wrexham
Nearest Police Station: Wrexham
Police Telephone Nº: (01978) 290211

GROUND INFORMATION

Ground Capacity: 1,000
Seating Capacity: 60+
Record Attendance: 300 (approximately)
Pitch Size: 110 x 72 yards

ADMISSION INFO (2005/2006 PRICES)

Adult Standing: £2.00
Adult Seating: £2.00
Child Standing: £1.00
Child Seating: £1.00
Programme Price: £1.00

DISABLED SUPPORTERS INFORMATION

Wheelchairs: Accommodated
Disabled Toilets: Yes
Contact Number: (01978) 855354

Travelling Supporters' Information:
Routes: Leave the A483 at the Rossett roundabout (B5102) heading towards Rossett. At the next roundabout turn right onto the B5445 and follow the road through Marford into Gresford. Turn right at the Plough Inn into the High Street then left before the Village Pond to the Village Memorial Hall for the ground.

GUILSFIELD FC

Founded: 1957
Former Names: None
Nickname: 'Guils'
Ground: The Community Ground,
The Community Centre, Guilsfield, Powys, SY21 9ND
Ground Telephone Nº: None

Colours: Red and Black shirts with Black shorts
Correspondence: S.J. Pearce, Lynian House,
Maes-Y-Rhiw, Berriew, near Welshpool SY21 8PL
Contact Telephone Nº: (01686) 640804
Fax Number: None
Web Site: www.guilsfield-fc.freeserve.co.uk
E-mail: team@guilsfield-fc.freeserve.co.uk

GENERAL INFORMATION

Club Shop: In the Refreshments Shop (Matchdays only)
Car Parking: At the ground
Coach Parking: At the ground
Nearest Railway Station: Welshpool (3 miles)
Nearest Bus Station: Oswestry
Nearest Police Station: Welshpool
Police Telephone Nº: (01938) 552345

GROUND INFORMATION

Ground Capacity: 1,000
Seating Capacity: 55
Record Attendance: Not known
Pitch Size: 115 x 75 yards

ADMISSION INFO (2005/2006 PRICES)

Adult Standing: £2.00
Adult Seating: £2.00
Child Standing: Free of charge for Under 16s
Child Seating: Free of charge for Under 16s
Concessionary Standing: £1.00
Concessionary Seating: £1.00
Programme Price: £1.00

DISABLED SUPPORTERS INFORMATION

Wheelchairs: Accommodated
Disabled Toilets: None
Contact Number: (01938) 554537

Travelling Supporters' Information:
Routes: Take the A490 from Welshpool and the first turn-off on the right into Guilsfield. The ground is situated on the left next to the School, directly at the side of Welshpool Road.

37

HALKYN UNITED FC

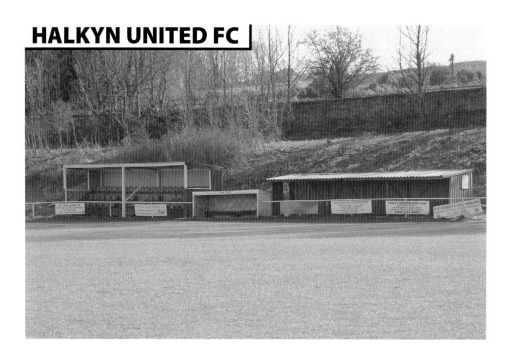

Founded: 1945
Former Names: Halykn Rangers FC
Nickname: None
Ground: Pant Newydd, Halkyn Cricket Club, Halkyn Road, Pentre Halkyn, Flintshire
Ground Telephone Nº: (01352) 780576

Colours: Blue shirts and shorts
Correspondence Address: Brian Pugh, 7 Hafan Deg, Holway, Holywell CH8 7DB
Contact Tel. Nº: (01352) 710431
Fax Number: (01352) 710431
Web Site: www.halkynunitedfc.co.uk

GENERAL INFORMATION

Social Club Telephone Nº: (01352) 780576
Club Shop: None
Car Parking: At the ground
Coach Parking: At the ground
Nearest Railway Station: Flint (6 miles)
Nearest Bus Station: Mold
Nearest Police Station: Colwyn Bay
Police Telephone Nº: (01352) 752321

GROUND INFORMATION

Ground Capacity: 1,000
Seating Capacity: 75
Record Attendance: 183 (vs Caerleon, February 2000)
Pitch Size: 110 x 75 yards

ADMISSION INFO (2005/2006 PRICES)

Adult Standing: £3.00 (includes programme)
Adult Seating: £3.00 (includes programme)
Child Standing: £1.00
Child Seating: £1.00
Senior Citizen Standing: £2.00 (includes programme)
Senior Citizen Seating: £2.00 (includes programme)
Programme Price: £1.00

DISABLED SUPPORTERS INFORMATION

Wheelchairs: Accommodated
Disabled Toilets: Available
Contact Number: (01352) 780576

Travelling Supporters' Information:
Routes: From Chester: Take the A55 to the turn-off for Rhosemor (B5123) and turn left at the Springfield Hotel to the top of the hill. Bear left and approximately ½ mile along after the double bend, the entrance gates to the Cricket Club are on the left hand side opposite the entrance to Halkyn Hall; From Conwy: Take the A55 to the Rhosemor (B5123) turn-off and turn right at the junction. After 200 yards turn right before the Haven Garage under the A55 and continue along to the Springfield Hotel. Then as above.

HOLYHEAD HOTSPUR FC

Founded: 1990
Former Names: None
Nickname: None
Ground: New Oval, Leisure Centre, Kingsland, Holyhead, Anglesey
Ground Telephone Nº: (01407) 764111
Colours: Blue & White striped shirts, Navy Blue shorts

Correspondence Address: Mr R. Parry, 27 Tan y Bryn Road, Holyhead   LL65 1AR
Contact Telephone Nº: (01407) 762904
Contact E-mail: richard@shirleyparry.wanadoo.co.uk
Alternative Contact: Gareth Davies (01407) 760576
Web site: www.holyhead.com/holyheadhotspur

GENERAL INFORMATION

Club Shop: At the ground
Car Parking: At the ground
Coach Parking: At the ground
Nearest Railway Station: Holyhead (½ mile)
Nearest Bus Station: Holyhead (½ mile)
Nearest Police Station: Holyhead
Police Telephone Nº: (01407) 762323

GROUND INFORMATION

Ground Capacity: 1,500 (covered standing for 500)
Seating Capacity: 80 (all covered)
Record Attendance: 1,200
Pitch Size: 110 x 72 yards

ADMISSION INFO (2005/2006 PRICES)

Adult Standing: £2.50
Adult Seating: £2.50
Child/Senior Citizen Standing: £1.50
Child/Senior Citizen Seating: £1.50
Programme Price: £1.00

DISABLED SUPPORTERS INFORMATION

Wheelchairs: Accommodated
Disabled Toilets: Available
Contact Number: (01407) 764111

Travelling Supporters' Information:
Routes: Take the A55 dual carriageway into Holyhead, turn left at the first roundabout onto the B4545 Trearddur Road. The Leisure Centre and field is on the right ½ mile from the roundabout.

HOLYWELL TOWN FC

Founded: Circa 1880 (as Holywell FC)
Former Names: Holywell FC, Holywell Victoria FC, Holywell Arcadians FC and Holywell United FC
Nickname: 'The Wellmen'
Ground: Halkyn Road Ground, Halkyn Street, Holywell, Flintshire CH5 7NE
Ground Telephone N°: None

Club Colours: Red and White shirts with Red shorts
Correspondence Address: Mr Michael Beech, 21 Woodlands Close, Mold, Flintshire CH7 1UT
Contact Telephone N°: (07916) 322428
Fax Number: None

GENERAL INFORMATION
Club Shop: None
Car Parking: At the ground
Coach Parking: At the ground
Nearest Railway Station: Flint (4 miles)
Nearest Bus Station: Holywell (½ mile)
Nearest Police Station: Holywell
Police Telephone N°: (01352) 711669

GROUND INFORMATION
Ground Capacity: 3,000
Seating Capacity: 300
Record Attendance: Approximately 3,000
Pitch Size: 115 x 72 yards

ADMISSION INFO (2005/2006 PRICES)
Adult Standing: £3.00
Adult Seating: £3.00
Child Standing: £1.50
Child Seating: £1.50
Programme Price: £1.00

DISABLED SUPPORTERS INFORMATION
Wheelchairs: Accommodated
Disabled Toilets: Available
Contact Number: (01352) 711538

Travelling Supporters' Information:
Routes: From the Town Centre: Proceed down Halkyn Road past the Police Station and the ground is situated on the left down an approach road (clearly signposted) at the rear of the Health Centre; From South Wales, Merseyside and the South: Follow the A55 Expressway and follow signs for Conwy until you reach the Holywell sliproad, A5026. The ground is on the right after 1 mile.

LEX XI FC

Founded: 1965
Former Names: None
Nickname: None
Ground: Stansty Park, Mold Road, Summerhill, Wrexham, North Wales
Ground Telephone N°: None

Club Colours: Amber shirts and shorts
Correspondence: Mrs Margaret Morris, Lex XI FC, 23 Edwards Avenue, Brymbo, Wrexham   LL11 5AT
Contact Telephone N°: (01978) 755209
Fax Number: (01978) 755209

GENERAL INFORMATION
Club Shop: None
Car Parking: At the ground
Coach Parking: At the ground
Nearest Railway Station: Wrexham (2 miles)
Nearest Bus Station: King Street, Wrexham (1 mile)
Nearest Police Station: Wrexham
Police Telephone N°: (01978) 290222

GROUND INFORMATION
Ground Capacity: 2,000
Seating Capacity: 50
Record Attendance: 1,004 vs Wrexham (1989)
Pitch Size: 110 x 75 yards

ADMISSION INFO (2005/2006 PRICES)
Adult Standing: £2.00
Adult Seating: £2.00
Child Standing: £1.00
Child Seating: £1.00
Concessionary Standing: £1.00
Concessionary Seating: £1.00
Programme Price: 50p

DISABLED SUPPORTERS INFORMATION
Wheelchairs: Accommodated
Disabled Toilets: None
Contact Number: (01978) 844430

Travelling Supporters' Information:
Routes: The ground is situated on a triangular piece of land known as Stansty Park in between Summerhill Road and Mold Road on the outskirts of Wrexham, 2 miles from the Town Centre and 1 mile from Wrexham FC's Racecourse Ground.

LLANDUDNO FC

Founded: 1988
Former Names: Llandudno Town FC
Nickname: None
Ground: Maesdu Park, Builder Street West, Llandudno, Conwy
Ground Telephone N°: (01492) 860945

Club Colours: Black & White shirts with Black shorts
Correspondence: Joey Kincaid, 60 Cae-Clyd, Llandudno, Conwy   LL30 1BL
Contact Telephone N°: (01492) 874688
Web Site: www.llandudnotownfc.co.uk
E-mail: info@llandudnotownfc.co.uk

GENERAL INFORMATION
Club Shop: Yes – in the Clubhouse
Car Parking: At the ground
Coach Parking: At the ground
Nearest Railway Station: Llandudno (½ mile)
Nearest Bus Station: Llandudno
Nearest Police Station: Llandudno
Police Telephone N°: (01492) 860260

GROUND INFORMATION
Ground Capacity: 6,000
Seating Capacity: 130
Record Attendance: 1,600 vs Everton
Pitch Size: 110 x 70 yards

ADMISSION INFO (2005/2006 PRICES)
Adult Standing: £3.00
Adult Seating: £3.00
Child Standing: £1.00 (free when with an adult)
Child Seating: £1.00 (free when with an adult)
Concessionary Standing: £2.00
Concessionary Seating: £2.00
Programme Price: £1.00

DISABLED SUPPORTERS INFORMATION
Wheelchairs: Accommodated
Disabled Toilets: Available
Contact Number: (01492) 860945

Travelling Supporters' Information:
Routes: Take the A55 Expressway to the Llandudno Junction exit (next to the Conwy Tunnel) and take the 2nd exit at the roundabout for Deganwy (A546). Pass through Deganwy and head into Llandudno. After the Golf Course take a right hand turn before the railway bridge then 1st left into Builder Street West. The ground is on the right next to the coach park; Alternative Route: Take the A55 Expressway to the Betws-y-Coed/Llandudno turn-off. Follow signs for Llandudno (A470) and then follow the road to the Links Hotel roundabout. Turn left past the Rugby field and take the next right. The ground is on the right next to the coach park.

LLANDYRNOG UNITED FC

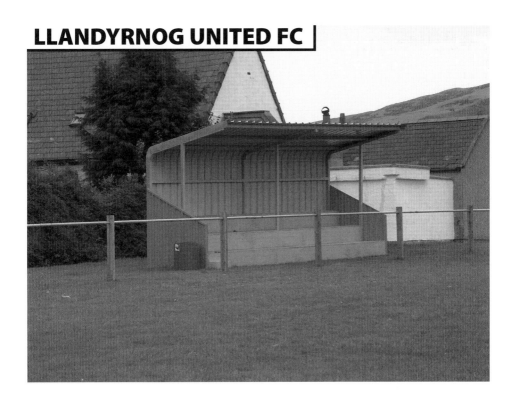

Founded: 1972
Former Names: None
Nickname: 'Dyrny'
Ground: Cae Nant, Llandyrnog, North Wales
Colours: Sky Blue shirts with Navy Blue shorts

Correspondence: Elis Jones, Groes Efa Bach, Llandyrnog, Denbigh LL16 4LT
Contact Tel. Nº: (01824) 790417
Fax Nº: None
Web Site: www.llandyrnogunited.co.uk
E-mail: elis@annwen.freeserve.co.uk

GENERAL INFORMATION

Car Parking: At the ground
Coach Parking: In the centre of the Village
Nearest Railway Station: Rhyl (16 miles)
Nearest Bus Station: Arriva service to the village available
Club Shop: None

GROUND INFORMATION

Ground Capacity: 1,000
Seating Capacity: 50
Record Attendance: Approximately 300 (during 2001)
Pitch Size: 110 x 75 yards

ADMISSION INFO (2005/2006 PRICES)

Adult Standing: £3.00
Adult Seating: £3.00
Junior Standing: £1.00
Junior Seating: £1.00
Programme Price: Included with entrance fee

DISABLED SUPPORTERS INFORMATION

Wheelchairs: Accommodated
Helpers: Admitted
Prices: Normal prices apply
Disabled Toilets: None
Contact Number: (01824) 790417

Travelling Supporters' Information:
Routes: Take the A542 from Mold or Denbigh to Bodfari then take the B5429 southwards (signposted Llandyrnog). After 3½ miles, go into the centre of the village and the ground is situated on the left down a narrow track just after the crossroads.

LLANFAIRPWLL FC

Founded: 1898 (Re-formed 1972)
Former Names: None
Ground: Gors Field, Llanfairpwll, Anglesey
Ground Telephone Nº: None
Colours: Light Blue shirts with White shorts

Correspondence: A. Mummery, 39 Trem Eryri,
Llanfairpwll, Anglesey
Contact Tel. Nº: (01248) 714938
Fax Number: None
Web Site: www.31cilygraig.freeserve.co.uk/Peldroed

GENERAL INFORMATION
Club Shop: At the ground – Matchdays only
Car Parking: At the ground
Coach Parking: At the ground
Nearest Railway Station: Llanfairpwll
Nearest Bus Station: Llanfairpwll
Nearest Police Station: Menai Bridge
Police Telephone Nº: –

GROUND INFORMATION
Ground Capacity: 750
Seating Capacity: 50
Record Attendance: 523 (during 2001)
Pitch Size: 110 x 70 yards

ADMISSION INFO (2005/2006 PRICES)
Adult Standing: £2.00
Adult Seating: £2.00
Child Standing: £1.00
Child Seating: £1.00
Programme Price: 50p

DISABLED SUPPORTERS INFORMATION
Wheelchairs: Accommodated
Disabled Toilets: Yes
Contact Number: (01248) 714938

Travelling Supporters' Information:
Routes: Take the A55 over the Menai Bridge and once across turn left towards Llanfairpwll. Pass the monument on the right, turn off for Plas Newydd on the left and head towards the Railway Station Centre. Just before the Railway Station Shopping Centre turn right into the car park for the ground.

LLANGEFNI TOWN FC

Founded: 1897
Former Names: Llangefni FC
Nickname: 'The Dazzlers'
Ground: Cae Bob Parry, Talwrn Road, Llangefni, Anglesey
Ground Telephone N°: (01248) 724999

Club Colours: Blue & Yellow shirts and shorts
Correspondence Address: Terry Roberts,
13 Bryn Tawel, Bryn Siencyn, Llanfairpwll, LL61 6RJ
Contact Tel. N°: (07733) 487886
Fax Number: (01248) 724165
Web site: www.llangefnitownfc.com
E-mail: john@cefni162.fsnet.co.uk

GENERAL INFORMATION
Club Shop: None
Car Parking: At the ground
Coach Parking: At the ground
Nearest Railway Station: Llanfair PG
Nearest Bus Station: Llangefni
Nearest Police Station: Llangefni
Police Telephone N°: (01248) 722222

GROUND INFORMATION
Ground Capacity: 2,000
Seating Capacity: 550
Record Attendance: 3,200 vs Man. United (14/11/2004)
Pitch Size: 110 x 75 yards

ADMISSION INFO (2005/2006 PRICES)
Adult Standing: £3.00
Adult Seating: £3.00
Child Standing: £2.00
Child Seating: £2.00
Programme Price: £1.00

DISABLED SUPPORTERS INFORMATION
Wheelchairs: Accommodated
Disabled Toilets: Available
Contact Number: (07733) 487886

Travelling Supporters' Information:
Routes: Take the A55 Expressway to Anglesey and exit at the Llangefni turnoff following the A5114 towards Llangefni. Before entering town, turn right at the Industrial Estate sign. Take the 1st exit at the roundabout and follow the road to the T-junction. Turn right and go past Kwik Save on the left. Follow the road up the hill past K.J. Forge Garage on the right and then turn left at the junction by the phone box into Talwrn Road (marked Pentraeth B5109). Continue for about ½ mile then turn left for the ground.

PENRHYN-COCH FC

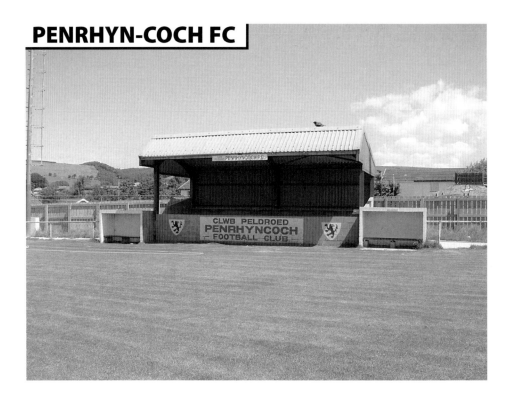

Founded: 1965
Former Names: None
Nickname: 'Penrhyn'
Ground: Cae Baker, Penrhyncoch, Aberystwyth, Ceredigion
Ground Telephone Nº: (01970) 828992

Club Colours: Red and Black shirts with Black shorts
Correspondence: Dr Michael Lee, The Illicit Still, 1 Sunnyside, Penrhyncoch, Aberystwyth SY23 3EH
Mobile Nº: (07971) 531001

GENERAL INFORMATION
Club Shop: Yes
Car Parking: At the Social Club
Coach Parking: At the Social Club
Nearest Railway Station: Aberystwyth (3 miles)
Nearest Bus Station: Aberystwyth (3 miles)
Police Telephone Nº: (01970) 612791

GROUND INFORMATION
Ground Capacity: 1,000
Seating Capacity: 50
Record Attendance: 350
Pitch Size: 113 x 75 yards

ADMISSION INFO (2005/2006 PRICES)
Adult Standing: £2.00
Adult Seating: £2.00
Child/Senior Citizen Standing: £1.00
Child/Senior Citizen Seating: £1.00
Programme Price: £1.00

DISABLED SUPPORTERS INFORMATION
Wheelchairs: Accommodated
Disabled Toilets: None
Contact Number: (07971) 531001

Travelling Supporters' Information:
Routes: From the North: Take the A487 from Machynlleth, through Talybont. Go through Bow Street, turning left at the A4157 and continue for ¼ mile. Turn left at the crossroads signposted for Penrhyncoch and 'Institute of Grassland & Environmental Research' (IGER). Follow the road for 1½ miles, bearing right at the village square and you will come to Penrhyncoch FC Social Club. Cae Baker is across the road from here; From the East: Follow the A44 from Llangurig to Aberystwyth. After travelling through Capel Bangor, turn right onto the A4159 signposted for Bow Street and Machynlleth (A487). After 1¾ miles turn right at the crossroads, signposted for Penrhyncoch and 'Institute of Grassland & Environmental Research'. Then as from the North.

QUEENS PARK FC

Founded: Around 1975
Former Names: None
Nickname: 'The Park'
Ground: Queensway Stadium, Queensway, Wrexham   LL13 8UH
Ground Telephone Nº: (01978) 355826

Colours: Blue & Maroon shirts with Blue shorts
Correspondence: Jonathan Halton, 4 Percy Road, Wrexham   LL13 7EE
Contact Telephone Nº: (01978) 350015
Fax Number: None

GENERAL INFORMATION

Club Shop: At Ragazzi in Wrexham town centre
Car Parking: At the ground
Coach Parking: At the ground
Nearest Railway Station: Wrexham (½ mile)
Nearest Bus Station: Wrexham (½ mile)
Nearest Police Station: Wrexham
Police Telephone Nº: (01978) 290222

GROUND INFORMATION

Ground Capacity: 1,000
Seating Capacity: 1,000
Record Attendance: Not known
Pitch Size: 110 x 72 yards

ADMISSION INFO (2005/2006 PRICES)

Adult Seating: £2.00
Child Seating: Free of charge
Concessionary Seating: £1.00
Programme Price: £1.00

DISABLED SUPPORTERS INFORMATION

Wheelchairs: Accommodated
Disabled Toilets: Available
Contact Number: (01978) 355826

Travelling Supporters' Information:
Routes: From the North and West: Take the A483 and the Wrexham bypass to the junction with the A541. Branch left at the roundabout, follow Wrexham signs into Mold Road then follow the brown athletics signs for the stadium; From the East: Take the A525 or A534 into Wrexham then follow the brown athletics signs for the stadium; From the South: Take the the M6, then the M54 and follow the A5 and A483 to the Wrexham bypass and the junction with the A541. Branch right at the roundabout, follow signs for the Town Centre then follow the brown athletics signs to the stadium.

RUTHIN TOWN FC

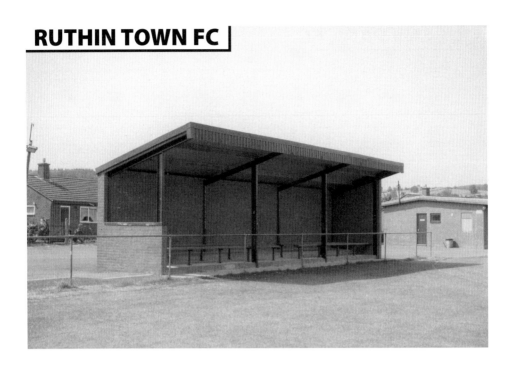

Founded: 1951
Former Names: Ruthin British Legion FC
Nickname: 'Town'
Ground: Memorial Playing Fields, Parc-y-Dre, Ruthin, Denbighshire
Ground Telephone Nº: None

Colours: Navy Blue shirts and shorts
Correspondence: Trevor Green, Glascoed, Bryneglwys, Corwen, Denbighshire LL21 9LF
Contact Telephone Nº: (01490) 450289
Contact E-mail: trevorgreen3@aol.com
Fax Number: None

GENERAL INFORMATION
Club Shop: None
Car Parking: At the ground
Coach Parking: At the ground
Nearest Railway Station: Rhyl
Nearest Bus Station: Rhyl – then Services 151/152
Nearest Police Station: Ruthin (1 mile)
Police Telephone Nº: (01824) 702041

GROUND INFORMATION
Ground Capacity: 2,000
Seating Capacity: 50
Record Attendance: 2,000
Pitch Size: 115 x 75 yards

ADMISSION INFO (2005/2006 PRICES)
Adult Standing: £3.00
Adult Seating: £3.00
Child Standing: 50p
Child Seating: 50p
Concessionary Standing: £1.00
Concessionary Seating: £1.00
Programme Price: 75p

DISABLED SUPPORTERS INFORMATION
Wheelchairs: Accommodated
Disabled Toilets: None
Contact Number: (07789) 022133

Travelling Supporters' Information:
Routes: The ground is situated on Park Road (A494). Turn into Parc-y-Dre next to the Fire Station and take the first right turn for the ground.

Welsh Premier League 2004/2005 Season	Aberystwyth Town	Afan Lido	Airbus UK	Bangor City	Caernarfon Town	Caersws	Carmarthen Town	Connah's Quay Nomads	Cwmbran Town	Haverfordwest County	Llanelli	NEWI Cefn Druids	Newtown AFC	Port Talbot Town	CPD Porthmadog	Rhyl	Total Network Solutions	Welshpool Town
Aberystwyth Town		1-1	1-0	1-2	5-0	1-0	0-0	1-0	0-1	4-0	2-0	2-1	1-1	0-0	0-0	1-2	1-1	0-0
Afan Lido	0-0		4-0	2-3	1-0	1-0	0-2	0-1	0-2	0-1	1-1	1-0	1-3	0-1	1-1	1-2	0-2	0-1
Airbus UK	1-2	1-4		0-0	1-1	0-3	0-1	3-3	0-1	1-2	0-3	1-2	2-2	3-1	0-1	1-0	0-6	0-2
Bangor City	4-2	1-0	5-0		2-0	1-0	0-1	2-0	0-3	1-1	6-0	2-0	2-3	3-2	0-2	2-1	1-0	4-2
Caernarfon Town	0-2	0-0	0-3	2-1		0-1	0-5	1-1	1-1	0-2	1-4	2-0	1-2	3-1	3-1	1-4	0-7	1-3
Caersws	4-1	4-1	3-0	2-2	3-1		1-2	1-2	5-2	1-0	2-0	7-0	2-0	2-2	0-1	1-4	0-0	2-1
Carmarthen Town	4-1	1-1	3-0	3-3	1-2	1-1		2-2	1-1	4-2	5-1	1-1	3-2	2-0	2-1	0-1	0-1	1-1
Connah's Quay Nomads	0-2	4-2	1-2	3-4	1-2	2-1	1-2		1-2	2-2	1-3	4-0	0-3	0-2	3-1	1-1	0-7	1-1
Cwmbran Town	2-3	1-0	4-4	0-3	2-1	1-4	0-2	1-0		0-2	2-0	3-3	1-2	3-1	2-1	0-1	2-2	2-3
Haverfordwest County	4-1	2-1	6-1	1-1	1-1	0-0	0-0	0-0	1-0		3-0	1-1	2-1	3-1	0-0	2-1	0-0	3-0
Llanelli	2-4	3-1	2-2	5-1	2-1	2-4	0-3	0-2	0-4	0-3		1-4	2-2	1-2	1-1	2-1	0-4	1-2
NEWI Cefn Druids	0-1	2-0	2-2	0-4	0-1	0-5	0-1	0-5	1-3	0-2	2-3		0-2	1-0	1-2	0-3	1-3	2-1
Newtown AFC	2-3	1-0	0-1	0-0	2-1	1-3	0-4	2-1	1-2	3-0	4-0	2-2		3-2	1-1	0-1	0-3	1-6
Port Talbot Town	0-1	1-2	3-2	1-4	0-0	0-1	0-0	2-2	1-1	0-1	4-0	1-1	0-0		1-2	1-3	2-2	3-0
CPD Porthmadog	2-0	2-0	3-3	3-0	2-0	0-1	3-2	0-0	1-1	0-2	1-1	0-0	0-2	1-0		0-3	1-2	1-1
Rhyl	1-0	3-1	2-0	2-3	5-1	3-0	3-1	4-2	0-0	0-0	2-0	3-2	3-0	1-0	3-1		1-2	2-2
Total Network Solutions	3-1	2-1	1-1	1-1	5-0	5-0	2-0	2-1	2-0	2-0	4-2	1-0	3-0	1-1	2-1	2-2		1-0
Welshpool Town	2-0	2-1	2-1	1-5	1-1	2-3	3-0	0-1	0-2	1-1	4-0	2-0	2-1	0-0	1-1	1-2	5-2	

Welsh Premier League

Season 2004/2005

Total Network Solutions	34	23	9	2	83	25	78
Rhyl	34	23	5	6	70	31	74
Bangor City	34	20	7	7	73	44	67
Haverfordwest County	34	17	12	5	50	28	63
Caersws	34	19	5	10	67	39	62
Carmarthen Town	34	17	10	7	60	34	61
Cwmbran Town	34	15	8	11	52	47	53
Aberystwyth Town	34	15	8	11	45	40	53
Welshpool Town	34	14	9	11	55	46	51
Newtown	34	13	7	14	49	55	46
CPD Porthmadog	34	11	12	11	38	39	45
Connahs Quay Nomads	34	9	9	16	48	58	36
Port Talbot Town	34	6	11	17	36	49	29
Llanelli	34	8	5	21	42	85	29
Caernarfon Town	34	7	7	20	29	72	28
Airbus UK	34	5	9	20	36	76	24
NEWI Cefn Druids	34	5	7	22	30	72	22
Afan Lido	34	6	6	22	29	52	21

Afan Lido had 3 points deducted

Cymru Alliance 2004/2005 Season	Bala Town	Buckley Town	Cemaes Bay	Flint Town United	Glantraeth	Gresford Athletic	Guilsfield	Halkyn United	Holyhead Hotspur	Holywell Town	Lex XI	Llandudno	Llandyrnog United	Llanfairpwll	Llangefni Town	Mold Alexandra	Penrhyncoch	Ruthin Town
Bala Town	■	1-2	5-0	6-0	3-2	2-1	2-4	1-0	1-2	2-1	3-2	1-0	1-0	3-2	1-0	3-0	1-1	1-2
Buckley Town	0-0	■	7-0	1-1	1-1	3-2	2-0	6-1	1-1	1-0	0-0	3-1	3-1	7-0	0-3	3-2	3-2	3-1
Cemaes Bay	1-5	1-3	■	0-4	1-3	1-5	1-7	1-5	0-2	1-4	0-9	2-6	3-3	1-3	0-4	2-2	1-4	0-2
Flint Town United	0-2	1-2	2-3	■	1-1	5-1	1-1	4-3	2-1	2-2	0-0	1-1	1-3	0-1	2-2	2-1	3-0	4-1
Glantraeth	4-0	3-0	3-0	1-0	■	0-1	6-0	3-2	2-1	2-1	4-1	1-1	3-1	1-2	0-3	7-0	2-0	3-0
Gresford Athletic	2-2	1-3	8-3	3-0	1-3	■	2-2	3-3	1-1	2-2	1-3	3-1	3-0	0-2	0-5	0-2	3-1	2-0
Guilsfield	0-2	0-0	8-0	2-1	3-0	0-3	■	2-0	1-2	2-3	3-2	3-3	3-2	1-1	4-1	3-2	1-1	0-1
Halkyn United	1-1	1-1	8-2	0-1	0-4	4-2	1-3	■	4-3	2-0	2-3	2-6	2-0	0-0	1-2	4-1	2-0	3-0
Holyhead Hotspur	2-3	1-2	3-1	2-1	2-1	1-4	4-3	2-0	■	0-2	1-5	1-2	1-1	1-2	1-0	2-0	1-1	0-1
Holywell Town	2-1	0-1	7-0	1-1	0-4	0-3	2-4	4-1	7-0	■	4-3	4-2	5-7	4-1	2-2	3-2	5-1	0-1
Lex XI	2-1	1-4	6-1	4-0	1-1	1-3	1-1	2-3	2-2	4-1	■	4-4	2-5	2-3	0-2	4-0	1-0	4-0
Llandudno	0-0	0-1	3-1	2-2	0-5	3-0	6-1	1-3	0-2	0-0	2-4	■	5-1	1-0	0-1	1-1	5-1	3-0
Llandyrnog United	4-1	0-1	3-1	0-3	2-2	3-1	1-0	4-1	0-1	3-2	0-1	5-0	■	2-0	1-3	5-0	1-2	2-3
Llanfairpwll	0-0	2-5	2-0	2-2	0-5	0-2	3-3	2-2	3-1	3-1	2-3	1-1	2-2	■	0-2	3-2	5-2	4-4
Llangefni Town	1-0	3-5	3-0	3-0	1-1	2-0	2-0	4-1	2-0	2-1	1-2	1-2	0-2	4-1	■	3-1	1-2	3-1
Mold Alexandra	0-1	3-0	6-0	2-1	0-1	2-4	1-5	3-3	2-0	1-1	3-4	0-0	0-2	4-1	0-1	■	2-2	2-1
Penrhyncoch	0-3	1-1	7-0	2-1	3-3	2-0	4-3	2-3	1-1	2-5	1-1	4-1	1-2	3-3	0-0	5-3	■	3-3
Ruthin Town	3-1	1-2	9-3	1-1	1-2	0-3	3-5	1-3	5-1	1-1	2-2	2-3	1-3	2-1	2-2	1-1	1-1	■

HGF Cymru Alliance

Season 2004/2005

Buckley Town	34	23	8	3	77	36	77
Glantraeth	34	21	7	6	84	33	70
Llangefni Town	34	21	5	8	69	33	68
Bala Town	34	18	6	10	60	41	60
Lex XI	34	16	8	10	86	60	56
Llandyrnog United	34	16	4	14	71	58	52
Guilsfield	34	14	8	12	78	66	50
Gresford Athletic	34	15	5	14	70	62	50
Holywell Town	34	13	7	14	77	64	46
Halkyn United	34	13	6	15	71	74	45
Holyhead Hotspur	34	12	6	16	46	63	42
Llanfairpwll	34	11	9	14	55	73	42
Ruthin Town	34	11	7	16	57	70	40
Penrhyncoch	34	9	12	13	62	71	39
Flint Town United	34	9	11	14	50	57	38
Llandudno	34	12	10	12	66	61	37
Mold Alexandra	34	7	7	20	51	78	28
Cemaes Bay	34	1	2	31	31	161	2

Cemaes Bay had 3 points deducted
Llandudno had 9 points deducted

Welsh Football League Division One

Season 2004/2005

Ton Pentre	34	24	7	3	91	34	79
Grange Quins	34	23	4	7	76	23	73
AFC Llwydcoed	34	20	6	8	65	35	66
Skewen Athletic	34	17	8	9	56	32	59
Goytre United	34	17	7	10	63	48	58
Maesteg Park	34	18	3	13	58	47	57
Bridgend Town	34	16	8	10	60	43	56
Taffs Well	34	15	6	13	71	48	51
UWIC	34	15	6	13	65	49	51
Briton Ferry Athletic	34	15	4	15	59	55	49
Barry Town	34	14	5	15	47	45	47
Bettws	34	14	5	15	47	51	47
Caerleon	34	11	11	12	44	47	44
Ely Rangers	34	11	5	18	54	62	38
Dinas Powys	34	10	8	16	43	51	38
Neath AFC	34	10	4	20	38	71	31
Gwynfi United	34	2	4	28	27	124	7
Garw	34	3	1	30	12	111	7

Welsh Football League Division Two

Season 2004/2005

Pontardawe Town	34	24	7	3	88	32	79
Newport YMCA	34	23	6	5	89	35	75
Bryntirion Athletic	34	23	2	9	79	40	71
Tredegar Town	34	21	5	8	64	37	68
Pontypridd Town	34	20	6	8	79	44	66
Garden Village	34	17	8	9	60	55	59
Penrhiwceiber Rangers	34	13	12	9	66	56	48
Caldicot Town	34	14	4	16	47	48	46
Porthcawl Town	34	12	8	14	43	52	44
Merthyr Saints	34	12	4	18	51	59	40
Pontyclun	34	11	5	18	47	56	38
ENTO Aberaman	34	11	4	19	44	75	37
Morriston Town	34	10	6	18	43	58	36
Tillery	34	11	1	22	51	98	34
Cardiff Corinthians	34	9	6	19	40	72	33
Ammanford	34	8	8	18	46	65	32
Seven Sisters	34	8	7	19	41	71	31
Llanwern	34	6	7	21	44	69	25

Welsh Football League Division Three

Season 2004/2005

Troedyrhiw	34	34	7	3	79	27	79
Croesyceiliog	34	23	6	5	81	35	75
Caerau Ely	34	20	7	7	80	50	67
Treharris Athletic	34	19	7	8	85	49	64
Chepstow Town	34	15	7	12	72	66	52
AFC Porth	34	15	7	12	58	59	52
Penrhiwfer	34	14	5	15	74	74	47
Treowen Stars	34	14	5	15	53	59	47
Pentwyn Dynamoes	34	13	6	15	73	76	45
Goytre FC	34	12	7	15	53	59	43
Blaenrhondda	34	12	7	15	50	60	43
Llantwit Fardre	34	12	6	16	62	61	42
Ystradgynlais	34	11	9	14	63	67	42
Cwmamman United	34	11	6	17	49	59	39
Newcstle Emlyn	34	10	6	18	72	102	36
Risca & Gelli	34	7	11	16	32	52	32
Albion Rovers	34	8	5	21	52	89	29
Fields Park Pontllanfraith	34	6	6	22	43	87	24

THE WELSH FOOTBALL LEAGUE

Address

Ken Tucker, 16 The Parade,
Merthyr Tydfil   CF47 0ET

Phone (01685) 723884   **Fax** (01685) 723884

AFAN LIDO FC

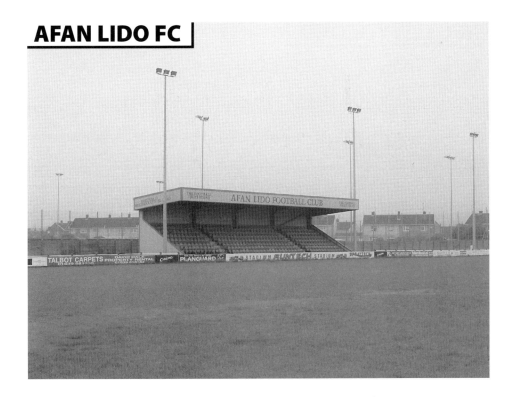

Founded: 1967
Former Names: None
Nickname: None
Ground: Afan Lido Football Ground,
Princess Margaret Way, Port Talbot
Ground Telephone Nº: (01639) 892960
Office Telephone Nº: (01639) 881432
Office Fax Nº: (01639) 881432

Colours: Shirts are Red with White trim, Red shorts
Correspondence Address: P. Robinson,
56 Abbeyville Avenue, Sandfields Estate, Port Talbot,
SA12 6PY
Contact Telephone Nº: (01639) 885638
Web site: www.afanlidofc.co.uk
E-mail: afanlidofc@aol.com

GENERAL INFORMATION

Club Shop: Yes – at the ground
Car Parking: At the ground
Coach Parking: At the ground
Nearest Railway Station: Port Talbot Parkway
Nearest Bus Station: Port Talbot
Nearest Police Station: Sandfields, Port Talbot
Police Telephone Nº: (01639) 883101

GROUND INFORMATION

Ground Capacity: 5,000
Seating Capacity: 525
Record Attendance: 1,100
Pitch Size: 112 x 75 yards

ADMISSION INFO (2005/2006 PRICES)

Adult Standing: £4.00
Adult Seating: £4.00
Child Standing: £1.00
Child Seating: £1.00
Senior Citizen Standing: £2.00
Senior Citizen Seating: £2.00
Programme Price: £1.00

DISABLED SUPPORTERS INFORMATION

Wheelchairs: Accommodated
Disabled Toilets: Available
Contact Number: (01639) 881432

Travelling Supporters' Information:
Routes: Take the M4 and exit at Junction 40. Follow all signs to Aberavon Beach from the Station – past Aberavon Centre, along Water Street, Ysgythan Road and Victoria Road, right at Afan Lido.

AFC LLWYDCOED

Founded: 1948
Former Names: Llwydcoed Boys Club FC and Llwydcoed Welfare FC
Nickname: None
Ground: AFC Llwydcoed Welfare Ground, Merthyr Road, Llwydcoed, Aberdare   CF44 0YA
Ground Tel. Nº: (01685) 873924

Colours: Black & White striped shirts, black shorts
Correspondence: David Evans, 25 Sycamore Close, Landare, Aberdare   CF44 8YD
Contact Tel. Nº: (01685) 870422
Fax Number: (01685) 871541
Web site: www.afcllwydcoed.8m.com

GENERAL INFORMATION
Club Shop: c/o David Evans, 25 Sycamore Close, Landare
Car Parking: At the ground
Coach Parking: At the ground
Nearest Railway Station: Aberdare (2 miles)
Nearest Bus Station: Aberdare (2 miles)
Nearest Police Station: Trecynon

GROUND INFORMATION
Ground Capacity: 500
Seating Capacity: None
Record Attendance: 300
Pitch Size: 110 x 65 yards

ADMISSION INFO (2005/2006 PRICES)
Adult Standing: £3.00 (by programme)
Child Standing: £1.00 (by programme)
Senior Citizen Standing: £1.50 (by programme)
Programme Price: £1.00 – £3.00 (includes admission)

DISABLED SUPPORTERS INFORMATION
Wheelchairs: Accommodated
Disabled Toilets: Available
Contact Number: (01685) 870422

Travelling Supporters' Information:
Routes: Leaving Neath on the A465, head towards Hirwaun. Take the 2nd exit at the 1st roundabout onto the Hirwaun Bypass then the 2nd exit at the next roundabout onto the A465 for Merthyr. At Baverstocks Hotel turn right onto the B4276 Llwydcoed/Aberdare Road. The ground is situated on the left after approximately 1½ miles.

BARRY TOWN FC

Due to problems beyond the club's control, fixtures for the 2005/2006 season will be played at Treforest and not at Jenner Park which is pictured above.

Founded: 1912
Former Names: None
Nickname: 'The Dragons'
Ground: White Tips Stadium, Kingsland Terrace, Treforest
Ground Telephone N°: (01443) 485532

Social Club Telephone N°: (01446) 735858
Club Colours: Yellow and Blue shirts, Yellow shorts
Correspondence: David Cole, 22 Goodwick Close, Lundy Park, Barry   CF62 9EF
Contact Telephone N°: (07970) 912348
Web site: None

GENERAL INFORMATION
Club Shop: None
Car Parking: At the ground
Coach Parking: At the ground
Nearest Railway Station: Treforest
Nearest Bus Station: Pontypridd
Nearest Police Station: Treforest

GROUND INFORMATION
Ground Capacity: 2,000
Seating Capacity: None
Record Attendance: Not known
Pitch Size: 110 x 70 yards

ADMISSION INFO (2005/2006 PRICES)
Adult Standing: £4.00
Child Standing: £2.00
Concessionary Standing: £2.00
Programme Price: £1.00

DISABLED SUPPORTERS INFORMATION
Wheelchairs: Accommodated
Disabled Toilets: Available
Contact Number: (01446) 735858

Travelling Supporters' Information:
Routes: Exit the M4 at Junction 32 and head north on to the A470. Take the exit signposted for the University of Glamorgan, Treforest and follow the one-way system. After passing under the railway bridge turn sharp right into Brook Street, bear left up the steep hill and turn right into King Street. The turning to the ground is on the left after the junction with Duke Street.

BETTWS FC

Founded: 1995
Former Names: Formed by the amalgamation of Bettws Athletic FC and Bettws AFC
Nickname: None
Ground: Bettws Park, North Site, Bettws, near Bridgend, Mid Glamorgan
Ground Phone Nº: (07887) 530804

Colours: Sky Blue shirts with Navy Blue shorts
Correspondence: Neil McEachen, The Old Post, Bettws Road, Bridgend   CF32 8TB
Contact Telephone Nº: (01656) 725381
Fax Number: (01656) 659319
Web site: www.bettwsfc.com

GENERAL INFORMATION

Clubhouse Phone Nº: (01656) 725618 (Oddfellows Arms)
Club Shop: At the Oddfellows Arms
Car Parking: At the ground
Coach Parking: At the ground
Nearest Railway Station: Bridgend (4 miles)
Nearest Bus Station: Bridgend
Nearest Police Station: Aberkenfig
Police Telephone Nº: (01656) 655555

GROUND INFORMATION

Ground Capacity: 1,000
Seating Capacity: None
Record Attendance: Approximately 800 (2001)
Pitch Size: 110 x 72 yards

ADMISSION INFO (2005/2006 PRICES)

Adult Standing: £3.00
Child Standing: £1.00
Concessionary Standing: £1.00
Programme Price: Included with admission

DISABLED SUPPORTERS INFORMATION

Wheelchairs: Accommodated in the Stand
Disabled Toilets: None
Contact Number: (07887) 530804

Travelling Supporters' Information:
Routes: Exit the M4 at Junction 36 and follow signs for Maesteg on the A4063. Go past the entrance to Sarn Park Services and at the roundabout take the 3rd exit signposted Maesteg (A4063). Continue until the traffic lights and turn right (signposted Bryn Cethin) onto the A4065. After ¾ mile pass under 2 railway bridges and pass the green on the right. Go straight on for 500 yards, turn left at the Bettws sign and follow the road into the village for 1½ miles. Pass the Oddfellows Arms and continue up the hill – the ground is situated on the left at the edge of the village.

BRIDGEND TOWN FC

Founded: 1954
Former Names: Bridgend Vics FC
Nickname: None
Ground: Coychurch Road, Bridgend, Mid Glamorgan
Ground Tel. Nº: (01656) 655097

Colours: Sky Blue & White shirts, Navy Blue shorts
Correspondence: Colin Mawer, Pine Lodge, Derwen, Bridgend CF35 6HD
Contact Tel. Nº: (01656) 650444
Fax Number: None

GENERAL INFORMATION

Club Shop: None
Car Parking: At the ground
Coach Parking: At the ground
Nearest Railway Station: Bridgend (¼ mile)
Nearest Bus Station: Bridgend
Nearest Police Station: Bridgend
Police Telephone Nº: (01656) 655555

GROUND INFORMATION

Ground Capacity: 5,000
Seating Capacity: 200
Record Attendance: Approximately 5,000
Pitch Size: 104 x 71 yards

ADMISSION INFO (2005/2006 PRICES)

Adult Standing: £2.00 (by programme)
Adult Seating: £2.00 (by programme)
Child Standing: £1.00 (by programme)
Child Seating: £1.00 (by programme)
Concessionary Standing: £1.00 (by programme)
Concessionary Seating: £1.00 (by programme)
Programme Price: Included in admission price

DISABLED SUPPORTERS INFORMATION

Wheelchairs: Accommodated
Disabled Toilets: None
Contact Number: (01656) 650444

Travelling Supporters' Information:
Routes: Exit the M4 at Junction 35 and bear left at the first roundabout. At the 2nd roundabout take the 3rd exit. Go past Tesco and Bridgend College on the left then turn right at the Fish & Chip shop into Coychurch Road. The ground entrance is approximately 100 yards on the right.

BRITON FERRY ATHLETIC FC

Founded: 1926/27
Former Names: None
Nickname: None
Ground: Old Road, Briton Ferry, Neath, West Glamorgan
Ground Telephone Nº: (07952) 777361

Club Colours: Green & Red shirts with White shorts
Correspondence: Martyn Thomas, 85 Glannant Way, Cimla, Neath SA11 3YW
Contact Telephone Nº: (01639) 767692
Contact Mobile Number: (07952) 777361

GENERAL INFORMATION

Club Shop: None
Car Parking: Street parking
Coach Parking: By Police direction
Nearest Railway Station: Neath (3 miles)
Nearest Bus Station: Neath (3 miles)
Nearest Police Station: Briton Ferry
Police Telephone Nº: (01639) 812220

GROUND INFORMATION

Ground Capacity: 2,000
Seating Capacity: 300
Record Attendance: 800 vs Abergavenny (1991/92)
Pitch Size: 112 x 75 yards

ADMISSION INFO (2005/2006 PRICES)

Adult Standing: £3.00 (by programme)
Adult Seating: £3.00 (by programme)
Child Standing: Free of charge
Child Seating: Free of charge
Programme Price: Included in admission

DISABLED SUPPORTERS INFORMATION

Wheelchairs: Accommodated
Disabled Toilets: None
Contact Number: –

Travelling Supporters' Information:
Routes: Take the M4 then the A48 and turn right at the roundabout for Briton Ferry then right again at the traffic lights and the ground is situated on the right; From Neath Railway Station: Turn right along Main Street, go under the subway at the junction, turn right into Briton Ferry Road, left into Cryddan Road and continue for 1½ miles past the Hospital. The ground is on the left.

BRYNTYRION ATHLETIC FC

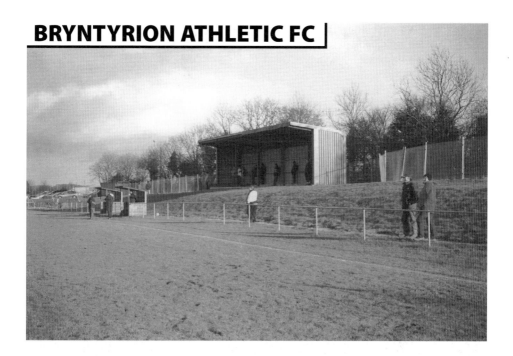

Founded: 1956
Former Names: None
Nickname: 'Athletic'
Ground: Bryntirion Park, Llangewydd Road, Bridgend CF31 4JU
Ground Telephone Nº: (01656) 652702

Club Colours: Blue shirts and shorts
Correspondence: Vic Carpenter, The Old Granary, Boverton, Llantwit Major CF61 1UH
Contact Tel. Nº: (07973) 829537
Fax Number: (01656) 652703
Web site: www.eteamz.com/bryntirionathletic/

GENERAL INFORMATION
Club Shop: None
Car Parking: Approximately 60 spaces at the ground
Coach Parking: At the ground
Nearest Railway Station: Bridgend
Nearest Bus Station: Bridgend
Nearest Police Station: Bridgend
Police Telephone Nº: (01656) 655555

GROUND INFORMATION
Ground Capacity: 1,000
Seating Capacity: None
Record Attendance: 400
Pitch Size: 120 x 87 yards

ADMISSION INFO (2005/2006 PRICES)
Adult Standing: £3.00
Child Standing: Free of charge
Programme Price: Included in the cost of admission

DISABLED SUPPORTERS INFORMATION
Wheelchairs: Accommodated
Disabled Toilets: Available
Contact Number: (01656) 652702

Travelling Supporters' Information:
Routes: Exit the M4 at Junction 35 and proceed left along the A48 towards Bridgend. Go straight on at 4 roundabouts (including a mini-roundabout) and continue for approximately 2 miles down the hill before turning left at the next roundabout, signposted for Laleston. Pass through the village and, after leaving the village, take the 1st turning on the left followed by the second left. Take the first left and go up the hill before turning right at the T-Junction. Then take the first left for the ground.

CAERLEON FC

Founded: 1889
Former Names: None
Nickname: None
Ground: Cold Bath Road, Caerleon, Gwent
Ground Telephone Nº: (01633) 420074

Club Colours: Green and White shirts and shorts
Correspondence: Mrs Jane Dean, The Gables,
Lodge Hill, Caerleon, Newport, Gwent   NP18 3BX
Contact Telephone Nº: (01633) 422264
Fax Number: None

GENERAL INFORMATION
Social Club Telephone Nº: (01633) 420074
Club Shop: None
Car Parking: At the ground
Coach Parking: At the ground
Nearest Railway Station: Newport (4 miles)
Nearest Bus Station: Newport
Nearest Police Station: Caerleon
Police Telephone Nº: (01633) 420222

GROUND INFORMATION
Ground Capacity: 1,200
Seating Capacity: None
Record Attendance: 1,000
Pitch Size: 117 x 74 yards

ADMISSION INFO (2005/2006 PRICES)
Adult Standing: £2.00 (by programme)
Child Standing: £2.00 (by programme)
Programme Price: £2.00 (includes admission)

DISABLED SUPPORTERS INFORMATION
Wheelchairs: Accommodated
Disabled Toilets: None
Contact Number: (01633) 420074

Travelling Supporters' Information:
Routes: From the East: Exit the M4 at Junction 25 and follow signs to Caerleon. In Caerleon at the junction of Lodge Road, turn left into Cold Bath Road for the ground.   From the West: Exit the M4 at Junction 25 and follow signs to Caerleon. Then as above.

DINAS POWYS FC

Founded: 1974
Former Names: Swan Stars FC
Nickname: None
Ground: Murchfield, Sunnycroft Lane, Dinas Powys
Ground Tel. Nº: None

Club Colours: Red & Black striped shirts, Black shorts
Correspondence: Rob Lewis, 9 Fulmar Close, Lavernock, Penarth CF64 5FE
Contact Tel. Nº: (029) 2070-5982
Fax Number: None
Web site: www.dinaspowysfc.co.uk

GENERAL INFORMATION

Club Shop: None
Car Parking: 30 spaces available at the ground
Coach Parking: None
Nearest Railway Station: Dinas Powys (¼ mile)
Nearest Bus Station: Cardiff Central (3½ miles)
Nearest Police Station: Barry
Police Telephone Nº: (01446) 734451

GROUND INFORMATION

Ground Capacity: 1,000
Seating Capacity: None
Record Attendance: Approximately 600 vs Bangor City
Pitch Size: 105 x 70 yards

ADMISSION INFO (2005/2006 PRICES)

Adult Standing: £3.00
Child Seating: Free of charge
Programme Price: £1.00

DISABLED SUPPORTERS INFORMATION

Wheelchairs: Accommodated
Disabled Toilets: Available
Contact Number: (029) 2051-4913

Travelling Supporters' Information:
Routes: Exit the M4 at Junction 33 onto the A4232 (3rd exit signposted Leckwith). Follow signs for Dinas Powys, turn left at the traffic lights by Dinas Powys Infants School, 2nd right into Camms Corner then 2nd right into Sunnycroft Lane. The ground is situated at the bottom of the road.

ELY RANGERS FC

Founded: 1965
Former Names: None
Nickname: 'The Griffins'
Ground: Station Road, Wenvoe, Cardiff
Ground Telephone Nº: (029) 2059-8725

Colours: Black and Blue striped shirts, Black shorts
Correspondence: Bob Fry, 4 Fairmead Court,
Fairwater, Cardiff   CF5 3DD
Contact Telephone Nº: (029) 2056-6762

GENERAL INFORMATION
Club Shop: Yes
Car Parking: At the ground
Coach Parking: At the ground
Nearest Railway Station: Cardiff Central (6 miles)
Nearest Bus Station: Cardiff
Nearest Police Station: Fairwater
Police Telephone Nº: (029) 2022-2111

GROUND INFORMATION
Ground Capacity: 1,000
Seating Capacity: None
Record Attendance: Approximately 1,000
Pitch Size: 110 x 75 yards

ADMISSION INFO (2005/2006 PRICES)
Adult Standing: £3.00
Child Standing: £1.00
Concessionary Standing: £1.00
Programme Price: 50p

DISABLED SUPPORTERS INFORMATION
Wheelchairs: Accommodated
Disabled Toilets: None
Contact Number: (029) 2056-6762

Travelling Supporters' Information:
Routes: Exit the M4 at Junction 33 and take the A4232 following signs for Cardiff Wales Airport. At Culverhouse Cross roundabout take the 3rd exit onto the A4050 Barry/Cardiff Wales Airport road. Go straight on at three mini-roundabouts and turn left in front of the grey footbridge over the road. This road is Station Road Wenvoe and the ground is 400 yards on the right.

GOYTRE UNITED FC

Founded: 1963
Former Names: None
Nickname: 'Goyts'
Ground: Glenhafod Park Stadium, Goytre, Port Talbot, West Glamorgan
Ground Telephone N°: (01639) 895615

Colours: Blue and White shirts with Blue shorts
Correspondence: Lyndon Suhanski, Stoneydale, Parc Pen y Bryn, Goytre, Port Talbot   SA13 2XZ
Contact Telephone N°: (01639) 894805
Fax Number: (01639) 898983
Web site: www.goytreutdafc.co.uk
E-mail: goytreunitedafc@aol.com

GENERAL INFORMATION
Club Shop: Yes
Car Parking: At the ground
Coach Parking: At the ground
Nearest Railway Station: Port Talbot General (1½ miles)
Nearest Bus Station: Port Talbot General (2 miles)
Nearest Police Station: Port Talbot
Police Telephone N°: (01639) 883101

GROUND INFORMATION
Ground Capacity: 4,000
Seating Capacity: 300
Record Attendance: Not known
Pitch Size: 110 x 70 yards

ADMISSION INFO (2005/2006 PRICES)
Adult Standing: £3.00
Adult Seating: £3.00
Child Standing: £1.00
Child Seating: £1.00
Concessionary Standing: £1.00
Concessionary Seating: £1.00
Programme Price: £1.00

DISABLED SUPPORTERS INFORMATION
Wheelchairs: Accommodated
Disabled Toilets: None
Contact Number: (01639) 898983

Travelling Supporters' Information:
Routes: Exit the M4 at Junction 40, bear left at the mini-roundabout and follow signs for Goytre. Turn left at the T-junction, pass through the village and the ground is down the hill on the left after approximately ½ mile.

MAESTEG PARK AFC

Founded: 1945
Former Names: Maesteg Park Athletic FC
Nickname: 'The Park'
Ground: Tudor Park, St. David's Place, Park Estate, Maesteg, Mid Glamorgan   CF34 9LR
Ground Telephone Nº: (01656) 730005

Colours: Blue and White shirts with Blue shorts
Correspondence: D. Griffiths, 3 Padley's Close, Maesteg, Bridgend   CF34 0TX
Contact Telephone Nº: (01656) 733000
Contact Mobile Nº: (07970) 824243
Fax Number: (01656) 733000

GENERAL INFORMATION

Social Club Telephone Nº: (01656) 730005
Club Shop: Yes and also a catering kitchen
Car Parking: At the ground
Coach Parking: At the ground
Nearest Railway Station: Maesteg (2½ miles)
Nearest Bus Station: Maesteg (2½ miles)
Nearest Police Station: Maesteg
Police Telephone Nº: (01656) 655555

GROUND INFORMATION

Ground Capacity: 2,000
Seating Capacity: None
Record Attendance: 1,000
Pitch Size: 112 x 78 yards

ADMISSION INFO (2005/2006 PRICES)

Adult Standing: £3.00 (by programme)
Child Standing: £1.00 (by programme)
Concessionary Standing: £2.00 (by programme)
Programme Price: Included in admission cost

DISABLED SUPPORTERS INFORMATION

Wheelchairs: Accommodated
Disabled Toilets: Available
Contact Number: (01656) 730005

Travelling Supporters' Information:
Routes: Leave the M4 at Junction 36 and take the A4063 to Maesteg. At the Cross Inn at Cwmfelin, turn left into the right hand lane up the steep hill. The ground is situated at the top of the hill on the left after passing the Red Cow pub on the right; On Foot: Take West Street from the Town Centre (turning off Commercial Street). Go up the hill for one mile then turn left at the junction. The ground is on the right.

NEATH ATHLETIC AFC

Founded: 1922
Former Names: National Oil Refineries FC,
BP Llandarcy FC and Neath FC (The current club
was formed when Neath FC amalgamated with
Skewen Athletic in 2005)
Nickname: 'The Oilmen'
Ground: Llandarcy Park Sports Ground, Llandarcy,
Neath, South Wales

Ground Telephone N°: (01792) 812036
Colours: Yellow and Black shirts with Black shorts
Correspondence: A.J.Melding, 15 Bosworth Road,
Skewen, Neath SA10 6BU
Contact Telephone N°: (01792) 812431
Web Site: www.neathathletic.ik.com

GENERAL INFORMATION
Social Club Telephone N°: (01792) 812036
Club Shop: None
Car Parking: At the ground
Coach Parking: At the ground
Nearest Railway Station: Skewen (2 miles)
Nearest Bus Station: Neath
Nearest Police Station: Neath
Police Telephone N°: (01639) 635321

GROUND INFORMATION
Ground Capacity: 1,500
Seating Capacity: 252
Record Attendance: Not known
Pitch Size: 110 x 75 yards

ADMISSION INFO (2005/2006 PRICES)
Adult Standing: £3.00
Adult Seating: £3.00
Child Standing: £1.50
Child Seating: £1.50
Programme Price: 50p

DISABLED SUPPORTERS INFORMATION
Wheelchairs: Accommodated
Disabled Toilets: Available
The Blind: No special facilities
Contact Number: (01792) 812036

Travelling Supporters' Information:
Routes: From the East: Exit the M4 at Junction 43, take the 1st exit at the roundabout and after about 150 yards follow signs
for Llandarcy Park Sports Field to the right. Follow the road for the short distance to the ground; From the West: Exit the M4 at
Junction 43 and take the 3rd exit at the roundabout. Then as above.

NEWPORT YMCA AFC

Founded: 1971
Former Names: Pill YMCA and Central YMCA
Nickname: None
Ground: Mendalgief Road, Newport
Ground Tel. Nº: (01633) 266872

Colours: Yellow and Blue shirts with Blue shorts
Correspondence: Viv Edwards, 100 Cardiff Road, Newport NP20 3AB
Contact Tel. Nº: (01633) 669001
Fax Number: None

GENERAL INFORMATION
Club Shop: None
Car Parking: At the ground
Coach Parking: Adjacent to the ground
Nearest Railway Station: Newport Central
Nearest Bus Station: Newport
Nearest Police Station: Cardiff Road, Newport
Police Telephone Nº: (01633) 244999

GROUND INFORMATION
Ground Capacity: 1,000
Seating Capacity: None
Record Attendance: Not known
Pitch Size: 110 x 65 yards

ADMISSION INFO (2005/2006 PRICES)
Adult Standing: £2.00
Child Standing: Free of charge
Programme Price: Included with admission

DISABLED SUPPORTERS INFORMATION
Wheelchairs: Accommodated
Disabled Toilets: Available
Contact Number: (01633) 266872

Travelling Supporters' Information:
Routes: Exit the M4 at Junction 28 and take Newport Road to the next roundabout. At the roundabout take the 2nd exit signposted for the Docks and follow the road under the railway bridge to the T-junction. Turn right and the ground is situated on the right hand side after 200 yards.

PONTARDAWE TOWN FC

Founded: 1947
Former Names: Pontardawe Athletic FC
Nickname: 'Ponty'
Ground: The Recreation Ground, Pontardawe, West Glamorgan
Ground Telephone Nº: (01792) 862228

Colours: Black and White shirts with Black shorts
Correspondence: Jonathan Wilsher, 14 Old Road, Neath   SA11 2BU
Contact Telephone Nº: (01639) 768557
Mobile Nº: (07831) 555464
Web site: www.pontardawetownafc.co.uk

GENERAL INFORMATION

Social Club: Gilberton Suite, Church Street, Pontardawe, West Glamorgan
Social Club Telephone Nº: (01792) 862230
Club Shop: None
Car Parking: At the ground
Coach Parking: At the ground
Nearest Railway Station: Neath (7 miles)
Nearest Bus Station: Pontardawe (¼ mile)
Nearest Police Station: Pontardawe (½ mile)
Police Telephone Nº: (01792) 456999

GROUND INFORMATION

Ground Capacity: 2,000
Seating Capacity: None
Record Attendance: 1,000 (vs Wrexham)
Pitch Size: 110 x 75 yards

ADMISSION INFO (2005/2006 PRICES)

Adult Standing: £2.50 (by programme)
Child Standing: £1.00 (by programme)
Programme Price: Included with admission

DISABLED SUPPORTERS INFORMATION

Wheelchairs: Accommodated
Disabled Toilets: None
Contact Number: (01792) 862228

Travelling Supporters' Information:
Routes: Exit the M4 at Junction 45 and take the A4067 to Pontardawe. Upon reaching Pontardawe, take the 1st exit at the roundabout across the river and at the next roundabout take the 3rd exit into Alloy Industrial Estate. The ground is situated at the far end of the Industrial Estate by a mini-roundabout.

TAFFS WELL FC

Founded: 1947
Former Names: None
Nickname: 'The Taffs'
Ground: Rhiw Dda'r, Parish Road, Taffs Well, Mid Glamorgan
Ground Tel. Nº: (029) 2081-1080

Club Colours: Yellow shirts with Black shorts
Correspondence: Norma Samuel, 103 Hillside Park, Taffs Well, Cardiff
Contact Tel. Nº: (029) 2081-3020
Fax Number: None
Web site: www.taffswellafc.co.uk

GENERAL INFORMATION
Club Shop: None
Car Parking: At the ground
Coach Parking: At the ground
Nearest Railway Station: Taffs Well
Nearest Bus Station: Cardiff
Nearest Police Station: Taffs Well

GROUND INFORMATION
Ground Capacity: 3,000
Seating Capacity: None
Record Attendance: 631
Pitch Size: 110 x 70 yards

ADMISSION INFO (2005/2006 PRICES)
Adult Standing: £3.00
Child Standing: Free of charge
Programme Price: £1.00

DISABLED SUPPORTERS INFORMATION
Wheelchairs: Accommodated
Disabled Toilets: None
Contact Number: (029) 2081-3020

Travelling Supporters' Information:
Routes: Exit the M4 at Junction 32 and take the A470 towards Merthyr. Then follow the B4052 to Taffs Well, pass through the village and over the 2nd railway bridge before taking the next turning on the right for the ground.

TON PENTRE FC

Founded: 1935
Former Names: None
Nickname: 'Bulldogs'
Ground: Ynys Park, Ton Row, Ton Pentre, Rhondda, South Wales
Ground Telephone N°: (01443) 442625

Clubhouse Telephone N°: (01443) 432813
Club Colours: Red shirts and shorts
Correspondence: P.Willoughby, 37 Bailey Street, Ton Pentre, Rhondda   CF41 7EN
Contact Telephone N°: (01443) 438281
Web site: www.tonpentreafc.com

GENERAL INFORMATION
Club Shop: Yes – at the ground
Car Parking: At the ground
Coach Parking: Llanfoist Street
Nearest Railway Station: Ton Pentre
Nearest Bus Station: Ton Pentre
Nearest Police Station: Ton Pentre
Police Telephone N°: (01443) 434222

GROUND INFORMATION
Ground Capacity: 2,700
Seating Capacity: 530
Record Attendance: 6,000 vs Falmouth
Pitch Size: 110 x 70 yards

ADMISSION INFO (2005/2006 PRICES)
Adult Standing: £4.00
Child Standing: £2.00
Concessionary Standing: £2.00
Programme Price: £1.00

DISABLED SUPPORTERS INFORMATION
Wheelchairs: Accommodated
Disabled Toilets: None
Contact Number: (01443) 442625

Travelling Supporters' Information:
Routes: Exit the M4 at Junction 34 and follow signs for Rhondda Valley and Treorchy. On reaching Ton Pentre, turn left over the railway bridge and then first left again for the ground.

UWIC INTER CARDIFF FC

Founded: 1951
Former Names: The club was formed by the amalgamation of University of Wales Institute Cardiff FC and Inter Cardiff FC in 2000.
Nickname: 'The Archers'
Ground: Cyncoed College, Cyncoed Road, Cardiff, CF2 6XD
Ground Tel. Nº: (029) 2041-6777

Club Colours: Yellow shirts with Blue shorts
Correspondence: A.E.Evans, 132 Lake Road East, Cardiff   CF23 5NQ
Contact Telephone Nº: (029) 2074-7122
Fax Number: (029) 2074-7738
Web Site: www.uwicsu.co.uk/main/auclubs/soccer
E-mail: alune@hw13.freeserve.co.uk

GENERAL INFORMATION

Club Shop: None
Car Parking: At the ground
Coach Parking: At the ground
Nearest Railway Station: Heath Halt (1 mile)
Nearest Bus Station: City Centre
Nearest Police Station: Llanedeyrn, Cardiff
Police Telephone Nº: (029) 2022-2111

GROUND INFORMATION

Ground Capacity: 2,000
Seating Capacity: 150
Record Attendance: 1,350 vs Everton, August 1996
Pitch Size: 110 x 72 yards

ADMISSION INFO (2005/2006 PRICES)

Adult Standing: £3.00
Adult Seating: £3.00
Child Standing: £1.00
Child Seating: £1.00
Concessionary Standing: £1.00
Concessionary Seating: £1.00
Programme Price: Included with admission

DISABLED SUPPORTERS INFORMATION

Wheelchairs: Accommodated
Disabled Toilets: Available
Contact Number: (029) 2041-6777

Travelling Supporters' Information:
Routes: Exit the M4 at the Cardiff Gate Link. After about 2 miles take the A48, Eastern Avenue. Head towards Cardiff and at the second interchange, take the 3rd exit. At the next roundabout take the 1st exit onto Llanedeyrn Road. After about 1 mile, take a right turn at the T-junction into Cyncoed Road and the ground is signposted on the right after about 1 mile.

ABERTILLERY EXCELSIORS FC

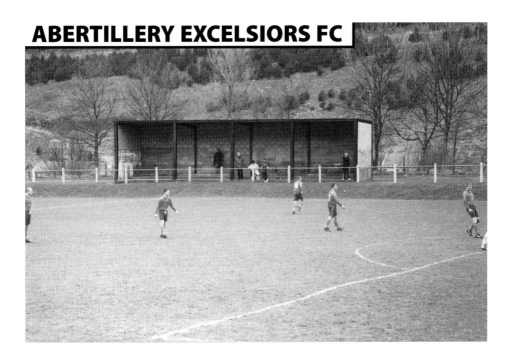

Founded: 1910
Former Names: Tillery FC, Cwmtillery Excelsiors FC, Cwmtillery AFC and Abertillery Town FC
Nickname: None
Ground: Woodland Field, Woodland Terrace, Cwmtillery, Gwent
Clubhouse Tel. Nº: (01495) 212732

Club Colours: Red shirts and shorts
Correspondence: Keith Williams, Ashfield House, Ashfield Road, Abertillery   NP13 1QE
Contact Tel. Nº: (01495) 212497
Fax Number: None
Web site: www.tilleryfc.ik.com

GENERAL INFORMATION
Social Club Telephone Nº: (01495) 212732
Club Shop: None
Car Parking: Limited number of spaces at the ground with a larger car park 500 yards away
Coach Parking: 500 yards from the ground
Nearest Railway Station: Abergavenny (14 miles)
Nearest Bus Station: Abertillery (1 mile)
Nearest Police Station: Abertillery
Police Telephone Nº: (01495) 212021

GROUND INFORMATION
Ground Capacity: 1,000
Seating Capacity: None
Record Attendance: Approximately 400
Pitch Size: 110 x 65 yards

ADMISSION INFO (2005/2006 PRICES)
Adult Standing: £2.00 (by programme)
Child Standing: 50p
Programme Price: £2.00 (includes admission)

DISABLED SUPPORTERS INFORMATION
Wheelchairs: Accommodated
Disabled Toilets: Available
Contact Number: (01495) 212497

Travelling Supporters' Information:
Routes: From the South: Exit the M4 at Junction 28 and take the A467 North to Abertillery. The ground is situated in Cwmtillery, just to the North of Abertillery; From the North: Take the Heads of the Valley Road A465 to Brynmawr then the A467 South to Abertillery for the ground.

AMMANFORD AFC

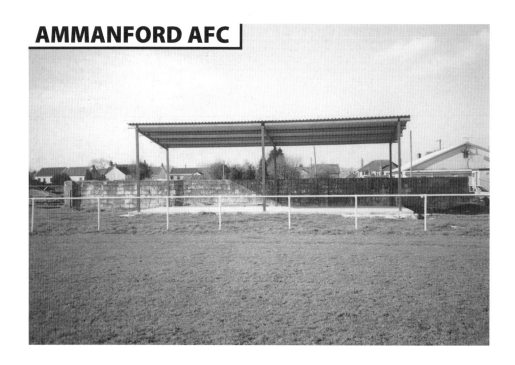

Founded: 1991 (Formed with the amalgamation of Ammanford Town FC & Ammanford Athletic FC)
Former Names: Betws FC
Nickname: 'The Town'
Ground: Betws Sports Club, Rice Road, Betws, Ammanford, Dyfed
Ground Tel. Nº: (01269) 592407

Colours: Black & White striped shirts, Black shorts
Correspondence: W.J.Thomas, 154 Hendre Road, Capel Hendre, Ammanford SA18 3LE
Contact Tel. Nº: (01269) 843712
Fax Number: None
Web site: www.ammanford-afc.co.uk

GENERAL INFORMATION
Club Shop: None
Car Parking: At the ground
Coach Parking: At the ground
Nearest Railway Station: Ammanford (½ mile)
Nearest Bus Station: Ammanford (½ mile)
Nearest Police Station: Ammanford
Police Telephone Nº: (01269) 592222

GROUND INFORMATION
Ground Capacity: 2,000
Seating Capacity: None
Record Attendance: 4,000
Pitch Size: 105 x 75 yards

ADMISSION INFO (2005/2006 PRICES)
Adult Standing: £2.00 (by programme)
Child Standing: £2.00 (by programme)
Programme Price: £2.00 (includes admission)

DISABLED SUPPORTERS INFORMATION
Wheelchairs: Accommodated
Disabled Toilets: None
Contact Number: (01269) 592407

Travelling Supporters' Information:
Routes: At the end of the M4 take the A483 then after approximately 5 miles turn right at traffic lights towards Betws. The ground is situated in Rice Road, Betws and is very hard to find!

CAERAU ELY AFC

Founded: 1955
Former Names: None
Nickname: None
Ground: Cwrt-yr-Ala, Ely, Cardiff
Ground Tel. Nº: (07790) 084636 (Matchdays only)

Club Colours: Red shirts with Black shorts
Correspondence: John Jarvis,
326 Cowbridge Road West, Ely, Cardiff
Contact Tel. Nº: (029) 2059-1969
Fax Number: None

GENERAL INFORMATION
Car Parking: At the ground
Coach Parking: At the ground
Nearest Railway Station: Cardiff Central
Nearest Bus Station: Cardiff Central
Nearest Police Station: Canton

GROUND INFORMATION
Ground Capacity: 1,000
Seating Capacity: 50
Record Attendance: Not known
Pitch Size: 105 x 72 yards

ADMISSION INFO (2005/2006 PRICES)
Adult Standing: £1.00 (by programme)
Adult Seating: £1.00 (by programme)
Child Standing: Free of charge
Child Seating: Free of charge
Programme Price: Included with admission

DISABLED SUPPORTERS INFORMATION
Wheelchairs: Accommodated
Disabled Toilets: None
Contact Number: (029) 2059-1969

Travelling Supporters' Information:
Routes: Exit the M4 at Junction 33, take the A4232 link road and pass the minor exit for the Museum of Welsh Life. Leave at the next exit (Culverhouse Cross) and take the 1st exit at the roundabout towards Cardiff on the A48. After approximately ½ mile, turn right into Heol Trelai, then right again into Caerau Lane then first left into Cwrt-yr-Ala Lane. Follow this road under the flyover for the ground.

CALDICOT TOWN FC

Founded: 1953
Former Names: Caldicot Playing Fields FC
Nickname: 'The Town'
Ground: Jubilee Way, Caldicot, Gwent
Ground Tel. No: (01291) 423519

Club Colours: Royal Blue shirts and shorts
Correspondence: John Burrows, 12 Heron Road, Caldicot   NP26 5RH
Contact Tel. No: (07752) 949913
Web site: www.caldicottownafc.co.uk

GENERAL INFORMATION
Club Shop: None
Car Parking: At the ground
Coach Parking: At the ground
Nearest Railway Station: Caldicot
Nearest Bus Station: Caldicot Town Centre
Nearest Police Station: Caldicot
Police Telephone No: (01291) 430999

GROUND INFORMATION
Ground Capacity: 1,500
Seating Capacity: None
Record Attendance: 600
Pitch Size: 110 x 75 yards

ADMISSION INFO (2005/2006 PRICES)
Adult Standing: £2.00
Child Standing: £1.00
Programme Price: 50p

DISABLED SUPPORTERS INFORMATION
Wheelchairs: Accommodated
Disabled Toilets: None
Contact Number: (01291) 431529

Travelling Supporters' Information:
Routes: Exit the M4 at Junction 23(A) Magor Services. Turn right at the roundabout and follow signs for Caldicot. At the 3rd set of traffic lights turn left and follow the road past the Petrol station. The car park for the ground is on the right after 200 yards, the Clubhouse and ground itself is on the left.

CARDIFF CORINTHIANS FC

Founded: 1898
Former Names: None
Nickname: 'Corries'
Ground: Riverside Ground, Thro' Stadium Road, Radyr, near Cardiff
Ground Telephone Nº: (029) 2084-3407

Club Colours: Cardinal & Gold shirts, Cardinal shorts
Correspondence Address: Gerry Thomas, 2 Lime Close, Radyr, Cardiff CF15 8EG
Contact Telephone Nº: (029) 2025-0167
Fax Number: None

GENERAL INFORMATION

Club Shop: None
Car Parking: At the ground
Coach Parking: At the ground
Nearest Railway Station: Radyr (adjacent)
Nearest Bus Station: Cardiff
Nearest Police Station: Cowbridge Road, Canton
Police Telephone Nº: (029) 2022-2111

GROUND INFORMATION

Ground Capacity: 1,000
Seating Capacity: None
Record Attendance: Not known
Pitch Size: 110 x 75 yards

ADMISSION INFO (2005/2006 PRICES)

Adult Standing: £2.00 (by programme)
Child Standing: Free of charge
Programme Price: Included with admission

DISABLED SUPPORTERS INFORMATION

Wheelchairs: Accommodated
Disabled Toilets: None
Contact Number: (029) 2084-3407

Travelling Supporters' Information:
Routes: Exit the M4 at Junction 32 and take the A470 signposted for Merthyr. After 1½ miles take the B4262 for Radyr. On entering the village (after approximately 2½ miles), turn left by the shops and go towards the Railway Station. Pass under the railway bridge, turn right and the ground is at the Radyr Cricket Club adjacent.

CROESYCEILIOG FC

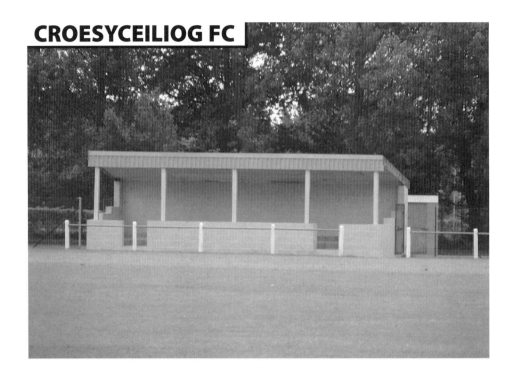

Founded: 1964
Former Names: None
Nickname: 'The Cockerels'
Ground: Woodland Road, Croesyceiliog, Cwmbran, Gwent
Ground Tel. Nº: (01633) 485157

Club Colours: Blue shirts and shorts
Correspondence: Martyn Jones, 8 Bath Green, Llanfrechfa, Cwmbran NP44 8US
Contact Tel. Nº: (01633) 863528
Web site: None

GENERAL INFORMATION
Car Parking: At the ground
Coach Parking: At the ground
Nearest Railway Station: Cwmbran (¼ mile)
Nearest Bus Station: Cwmbran (½ mile)

GROUND INFORMATION
Ground Capacity: 1,000
Seating Capacity: None
Record Attendance: Not known
Pitch Size: 110 x 70 yards

ADMISSION INFO (2005/2006 PRICES)
Adult Standing: £2.00
Senior Citizen Standing: £1.00
Child Standing: Free of charge
Programme Price: Included in admission price

DISABLED SUPPORTERS INFORMATION
Wheelchairs: Accommodated
Helpers: Admitted
Prices: Normal prices apply
Disabled Toilets: Available at the ground
Contact Number: (01633) 863528

Travelling Supporters' Information:
Routes: Exit the M4 at Junction 26 and take the A4051. Keep left on the dual carriageway signposted for Cwmbran and continue through 6 sets of traffic lights. At the roundabout take the A4042 signposted for Abergavenny and continue to the next roundabout then turn left. Follow the road to the next roundabout and follow signs for Abergavenny/Police Headquarters. Turn left at the following roundabout and continue down passing the County Hall and Police HQ on the right. Take the next left into Woodland Road by the Texaco petrol station and the ground is ¼ mile on the left behind the large conifers.

ENTO ABERAMAN ATHLETIC FC

Founded: 1892
Former Names: Aberaman Athletic FC
Nickname: 'Aber'
Ground: Aberaman Park, Aberaman, Aberdare, Mid Glamorgan
Ground Tel. Nº: (07966) 597567 (Matchdays only)

Club Colours: Royal Blue shirts and shorts
Correspondence: Brian Fear, 28 Mostyn Street, Abercwmboi, Aberdare CF44 6BB
Contact Tel. Nº: (01443) 472858
Mobile Nº: (07966) 597567
Web Site: www.aberamanafc.vze.com

GENERAL INFORMATION
Car Parking: At the ground
Coach Parking: At the ground
Nearest Railway Station: Cwmbach
Nearest Bus Station: Aberdare
Nearest Police Station: Aberdare
Police Telephone Nº: (01685) 872461

GROUND INFORMATION
Ground Capacity: 2,000
Seating Capacity: 160
Record Attendance: 10,000 (during World War II)
Pitch Size: 115 x 75 yards

ADMISSION INFO (2005/2006 PRICES)
Adult Standing: £2.50 (by programme)
Adult Seating: £2.50 (by programme)
Child Standing: Free of charge
Child Seating: Free of charge
Programme Price: £2.50 (includes admission)

DISABLED SUPPORTERS INFORMATION
Wheelchairs: Accommodated
Disabled Toilets: None
Contact Number: (01443) 472858

Travelling Supporters' Information:
Routes: Exit the M4 at Junction 32 and take the A470 signposted for Merthyr Tydfil. Continue on the A470 for approximately 10 miles and take the 1st exit at the roundabout onto the A4059 signposted for Aberdare. Follow this road to Mountain Ash. Before reaching the traffic lights and Town Hall, turn left (signposted Mountain Ash Town Centre) then turn right at the traffic lights (signposted Aberaman). Travel through the villages of Fernhill and Abercwmboi (approximately 2 miles). At the far end of Abercwmboi, the ground is on the right hand side just past the Motomec Garage and before the Kwik Save Store.

GARDEN VILLAGE FC

Founded: 1922
Former Names: None
Nickname: 'Village'
Ground: Stafford Common, Victoria Road, Gorseinon, Swansea   SA4 3AB
Ground Telephone Nº: (01792) 894933

Club Colours: Black & White shirts with Black shorts
Correspondence: Clive Greenfield, 5 Maple Close, Penyrheol, Gorseinon, Swansea   SA4 4XL
Contact Telephone Nº: (01792) 517298
Fax Number: None
Web Site: www.gardenvillageafc.tk

GENERAL INFORMATION

Club Shop: At the ground on matchdays only
Car Parking: At the ground
Coach Parking: At the ground
Nearest Railway Station: Gowerton (1 mile)
Nearest Bus Station: Gorseinon
Nearest Police Station: Gorseinon
Police Telephone Nº: (01792) 456999

GROUND INFORMATION

Ground Capacity: 2,000
Seating Capacity: None
Record Attendance: Not known
Pitch Size: 110 x 70 yards

ADMISSION INFO (2005/2006 PRICES)

Adult Standing: £2.00
Child Standing: Free of charge
Programme Price: 50p

DISABLED SUPPORTERS INFORMATION

Wheelchairs: Accommodated
Disabled Toilets: Available in the changing room block
Contact Number: (01792) 894933

Travelling Supporters' Information:
Routes: Exit the M4 at Junction 47 and follow signs for Swansea. Take the 2nd exit at the first roundabout signposted Llanelli and continue for one mile. Go straight on at the next roundabout, then take the 3rd exit at the following roundabout. Follow the road for ½ mile and the ground is situated on the right.

GARW FC

Founded: 1945
Former Names: Garw Athletic FC
Nickname: 'Athletic' 'Mountain Men'
Ground: Blandy Park, Pontycymer, near Bridgend, South Wales
Ground Telephone N°: None

Colours: Red shirts and shorts
Correspondence: Ray Smiles, 48 Blaengarw Road, Blaengarw, Mid Glamorgan
Contact Telephone N°: (01656) 870487
Fax Number: None

GENERAL INFORMATION
Club Shop: None
Car Parking: Street parking only
Coach Parking: Street parking only
Nearest Railway Station: Tondu (4 miles)
Nearest Bus Station: Bridgend (10 miles)
Nearest Police Station: Aberkenfig
Police Telephone N°: –

GROUND INFORMATION
Ground Capacity: 1,000
Seating Capacity: None
Record Attendance: 1,000 (1945 Cup Final – Army vs Blue Birds)
Pitch Size: 110 x 65 yards

ADMISSION INFO (2005/2006 PRICES)
Adult Standing: £2.00 (by programme)
Child Standing: Free of charge
Programme Price: £2.00 (included in admission)

DISABLED SUPPORTERS INFORMATION
Wheelchairs: Accommodated
Disabled Toilets: None
Contact Number: (01656) 871906

Travelling Supporters' Information:
Routes: Exit the M4 at Junction 36 and take the A4061 to Bryncethin. Turn left onto the A4064 and continue to Pontycymer. Upon reaching Pontycymer take the first left after the town sign for the ground.

GWYNFI UNITED FC

Founded: 1971
Former Names: Gwynfi Welfare FC
Nickname: None
Ground: Gwynfi Welfare, Blaengwynfi, Port Talbot, West Glamorgan
Ground Telephone N°: (01639) 852089

Club Colours: Green shirts with Black shorts
Correspondence: David Walters, 16 Pond Mawr, Maesteg   CF34 0NG
Contact Telephone N°: (07879) 670306
Fax Number: (01656) 812145

GENERAL INFORMATION
Social Club Telephone N°: None
Club Shop: None
Car Parking: At the ground
Coach Parking: At the ground
Nearest Railway Station: Port Talbot (10 miles)
Nearest Bus Station: Port Talbot (10 miles)
Nearest Police Station: Cymmer
Police Telephone N°: (01639) 883101

GROUND INFORMATION
Ground Capacity: 1,500
Seating Capacity: None
Record Attendance: Not known
Pitch Size: 110 x 71 yards

ADMISSION INFO (2005/2006 PRICES)
Adult Standing: £2.00 (by programme)
Child Standing: Free of charge
Programme Price: £2.00 (includes admission)

DISABLED SUPPORTERS INFORMATION
Wheelchairs: Accommodated
Disabled Toilets: None
Contact Number: (01639) 852089

Travelling Supporters' Information:
Routes: Exit the M4 at Junction 36 and follow the A4063 to Maesteg. Pass through Maesteg and take the A4107 towards Treorchy at Croeserw. Turn left after about 2 miles into Blaengwynfi for the ground.

MERTHYR SAINTS FC

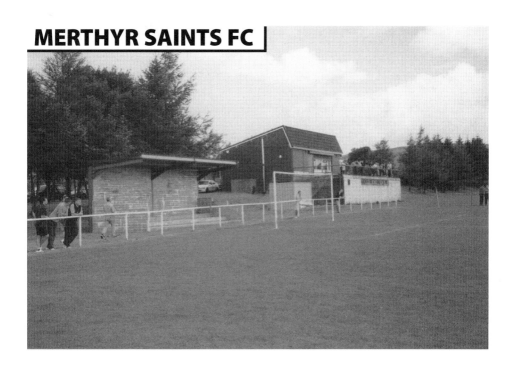

Founded: During the 1950s
Former Names: Hoover Sports FC
Nickname: 'Saints'
Ground: ICI Pavilion, Bryniau Road, Pant, Merthyr Tydfil
Ground Tel. Nº: (01685) 386140

Club Colours: Red shirts and shorts
Correspondence: Ron Jones, 6 Brunswick Street, Merthyr Tydfil   CF47 8SB
Contact Tel. Nº: (01685) 377871
Fax Number: None

GENERAL INFORMATION
Club Shop: At the ground
Car Parking: At the ground
Coach Parking: At the ground
Nearest Railway Station: Merthyr Tydfil (1½ miles)
Nearest Bus Station: Pant (adjacent)
Nearest Police Station: Dowlais

GROUND INFORMATION
Ground Capacity: 1,000
Seating Capacity: None
Record Attendance: 200
Pitch Size: 99 x 77 yards

ADMISSION INFO (2005/2006 PRICES)
Adult Standing: £2.50
Child Standing: Free of charge
Programme Price: 50p

DISABLED SUPPORTERS INFORMATION
Wheelchairs: Accommodated
Disabled Toilets: Available
Contact Number: (01685) 377871

Travelling Supporters' Information:
Routes: Take the 1st exit off the A465 'Heads of the Valleys Road' signposted for Prince Charles Hospital and head for the Brecon Mountain Railway Park. The ground is in Bryniau Road, adjacent to the Pant Industrial Park.

MORRISTON TOWN FC

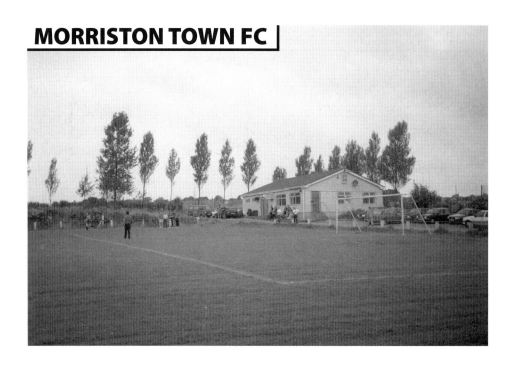

Founded: 1926
Former Names: Grove Mission FC and Midland Athletic FC
Nickname: None
Ground: Dingle Road, Morriston, Swansea
Ground Telephone Nº: (01792) 702033

Club Colours: Red shirts and shorts
Correspondence: David Bennett, 51 Severn Road, Clase, Morriston, Swansea SA6 7LQ
Contact Tel. Nº: (01792) 791713
Fax Number: None
Web site: None

GENERAL INFORMATION
Car Parking: At the ground
Coach Parking: At the ground
Nearest Railway Station: Swansea
Nearest Bus Station: Swansea
Nearest Police Station: Morriston
Police Telephone Nº: (01792) 771294

GROUND INFORMATION
Ground Capacity: 1,000
Seating Capacity: None
Record Attendance: Approximately 600 vs Swansea
Pitch Size: 104 x 74 yards

ADMISSION INFO (2005/2006 PRICES)
Adult Standing: £2.00 (by programme)
Child Standing: Free of charge
Concessionary Standing: £1.00 (by programme)
Programme Price: Included with admission

DISABLED SUPPORTERS INFORMATION
Wheelchairs: Accommodated
Disabled Toilets: None
Contact Number: (01792) 791713

Travelling Supporters' Information:
Routes: Exit the M4 at Junction 45 for Swansea and take the 2nd exit at the roundabout bearing left. The ground is situated ½ mile along this road on the right hand side behind the houses.

PENRHIWCEIBER RANGERS FC

Founded: 1961
Former Names: Penrhiwceiber Welfare FC
Nickname: None
Ground: Glasbrook Field, Glasbrook Terrace, Mountain Ash, Mid Glamorgan
Ground Telephone Nº: None

Club Colours: Red shirts and shorts
Correspondence: J.Dudley, 131 Abercynon Road, Abercynon   CF45 4NE
Contact Telephone Nº: (01443) 741433
Fax Number: None

GENERAL INFORMATION
Club Shop: None
Car Parking: Street parking
Coach Parking: Street parking
Nearest Railway Station: Penrhiwceiber (400 yards)
Nearest Bus Station: Penrhiwceiber
Nearest Police Station: Mountain Ash
Police Telephone Nº: –

GROUND INFORMATION
Ground Capacity: 3,000
Seating Capacity: 300
Record Attendance: Not known
Pitch Size: 110 x 72 yards

ADMISSION INFO (2005/2006 PRICES)
Adult Standing: £2.00
Adult Seating: £2.00
Child Standing: £1.00
Child Seating: £1.00
Concessionary Standing: £1.00
Concessionary Seating: £1.00
Programme Price: 50p

DISABLED SUPPORTERS INFORMATION
Wheelchairs: Accommodated
Disabled Toilets: None
Contact Number: (01443) 741433

Travelling Supporters' Information:
Routes: Exit the M4 at Junction 32 and follow signs for Merthyr (A470). Carry along the A470 to the end and exit at the roundabout for Abercynon West. Pass through Abercynon and after 1½ miles, the ground is on the right.

PONTYCLUN FC

Founded: 1896
Former Names: None
Nickname: 'The Clun'
Ground: Ivor Park, Cowbridge Road, Pontyclun
Clubhouse Tel. Nº: (01443) 222182

Club Colours: Yellow shirts with Blue shorts
Correspondence: Peter Shilton, 16 Castan Road, Pontyclun CF72 9EH
Contact Tel. Nº: (01443) 239658
Web site: www.freewebs.com/pontyclunfootballclub/

GENERAL INFORMATION

Social Club Telephone Nº: (01443) 222182
Club Shop: None
Car Parking: At the ground
Coach Parking: At the ground
Nearest Railway Station: Pontyclun (½ mile)
Nearest Bus Station: Talbot Green (2 miles)
Nearest Police Station: Talbot Green

GROUND INFORMATION

Ground Capacity: 1,000
Seating Capacity: None
Record Attendance: Approximately 500
Pitch Size: 105 x 72 yards

ADMISSION INFO (2005/2006 PRICES)

Adult Standing: £2.00 (by programme)
Child Standing: £1.00 (by programme)
Programme Price: Included with admission

DISABLED SUPPORTERS INFORMATION

Wheelchairs: Accommodated
Disabled Toilets: None
Contact Number: (01443) 239658

Travelling Supporters' Information:
Routes: Exit the M4 at Junction 34, take the A4119 towards Llantrisant and follow signs for Cowbridge. Pass Leekes DIY store on the left and pass through Pontyclun. The ground is on the left before the Ivor Arms public house.

PONTYPRIDD TOWN AFC

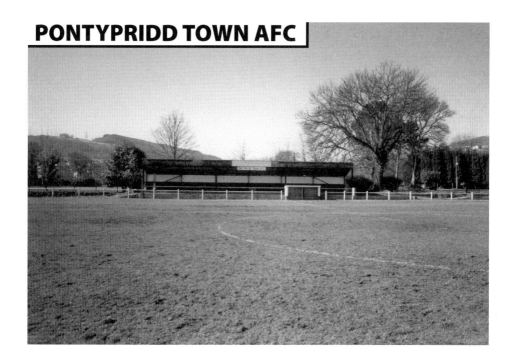

Founded: 1895
Former Names: Ynysbwl FC
Nickname: 'The Dragons'
Ground: Ynysangharad War Memorial Park, Pontypridd
Ground Tel. Nº: (01443) 486571

Colours: Black and White shirts with Black shorts
Correspondence: Alf Germain, 145 Buarth-y-Capel, Ynysybwl, Mid Glamorgan   CF37 1LE
Contact Tel. Nº: (01443) 791963
Fax Number: (01443) 791763
Web site: www.pontypriddtownfc.co.uk

GENERAL INFORMATION
Club Shop: None
Car Parking: Street parking only
Coach Parking: Street parking only
Nearest Railway Station: Pontypridd (½ mile)
Nearest Bus Station: Pontypridd (½ mile)
Nearest Police Station: Pontypridd
Police Telephone Nº: (01443) 485351

GROUND INFORMATION
Ground Capacity: 2,000
Seating Capacity: 150
Record Attendance: Not known
Pitch Size: 110 x 70 yards

ADMISSION INFO (2005/2006 PRICES)
Adult Standing: £3.00 (by programme)
Adult Seating: £3.00 (by programme)
Senior Citizen Standing: £2.00 (by programme)
Senior Citizen Seating: £2.00 (by programme)
Child Standing: Free of charge when with a paying adult
Child Seating: Free of charge when with a paying adult
Programme Price: £3.00 or £2.00 (includes admission)

DISABLED SUPPORTERS INFORMATION
Wheelchairs: Accommodated
Disabled Toilets: Available
Contact Number: (07786) 523577

Travelling Supporters' Information:
Routes: Take the A470 dual carriageway and exit at the Ynysybwl turn-off. The ground is situated adjacent to the A470 northbound in Ynysangharad War Memorial Park.

PORTHCAWL TOWN FC

Founded: 1947
Former Names: None
Nickname: 'Seasiders'
Ground: Locks Lane, Porthcawl, Mid Glamorgan
Mobile Contact N°: (07866) 545830

Colours: Shirts and shorts are Red with White trim
Correspondence: Steve Harris, 18 Mary Street, Porthcawl CF36 3YA
Contact Tel. N°: (01656) 786946
Fax Number: (01656) 785900

GENERAL INFORMATION
Club Shop: None
Car Parking: 100 spaces available at the ground
Coach Parking: At the ground
Nearest Railway Station: Bridgend (6 miles)
Nearest Bus Station: Bridgend (6 miles)
Nearest Police Station: John Street, Porthcawl
Police Telephone N°: (01656) 655555

GROUND INFORMATION
Ground Capacity: 1,000
Seating Capacity: None
Record Attendance: 2,000
Pitch Size: 100 x 67 yards

ADMISSION INFO (2005/2006 PRICES)
Adult Standing: £2.00
Child Standing: Free of charge
Programme Price: £1.00

DISABLED SUPPORTERS INFORMATION
Wheelchairs: Accommodated
Disabled Toilets: Available
Contact Number: (07866) 545830

Travelling Supporters' Information:
Routes: Exit the M4 at Junction 37 and take the first exit at the roundabout (signposted Porthcawl). Continue straight on at the 2nd roundabout then take the 3rd exit at the next roundabout onto the A4229. Take the 3rd exit at the next roundabout into Falmer Road travelling uphill. The road then bends sharply to the left and becomes Mallard Way. Continue along this road and turn first left into Locks Lane. The ground is then on the left.

TREDEGAR TOWN FC

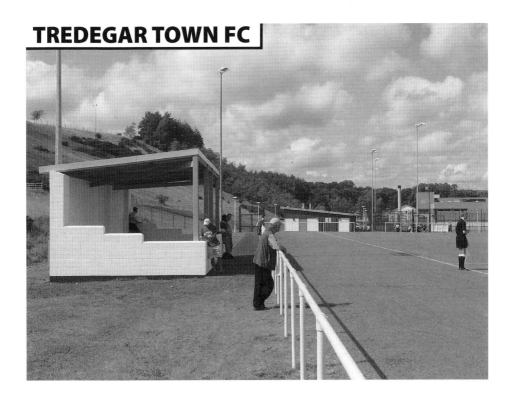

Founded: 1958
Former Names: None
Nickname: 'Town'
Ground: Tredegar Leisure Centre, Stable Lane, Tredegar, Gwent
Ground Tel. N°: (01495) 723554

Colours: Red shirts and shorts
Correspondence: Riley Gray, 7 Gladstone Place, Tredegar NP22 4LG
Contact Tel. N°: (01495) 723554
Fax Number: None

GENERAL INFORMATION

Car Parking: At the Leisure Centre Complex
Coach Parking: At the Leisure Centre Complex
Nearest Railway Station: Rhymney (1 mile)
Nearest Bus Station: Tredegar
Nearest Police Station: Tredegar

GROUND INFORMATION

Ground Capacity: 1,000
Seating Capacity: None
Record Attendance: Approximately 300
Pitch Size: 120 x 77 yards

ADMISSION INFO (2005/2006 PRICES)

Adult Standing: £2.00
Adult Seating: £2.00
Child Standing: £1.00
Child Seating: £1.00
Programme Price: Included in admission price

DISABLED SUPPORTERS INFORMATION

Wheelchairs: Accommodated
Disabled Toilets: Available
Contact Number: (01495) 723554

Travelling Supporters' Information:
Routes: Take the A4048 to Tredegar. The Leisure Centre Complex is situated in the Southern part of Tredegar in Stable Lane which is just off the A4048.

TROEDYRHIW FC

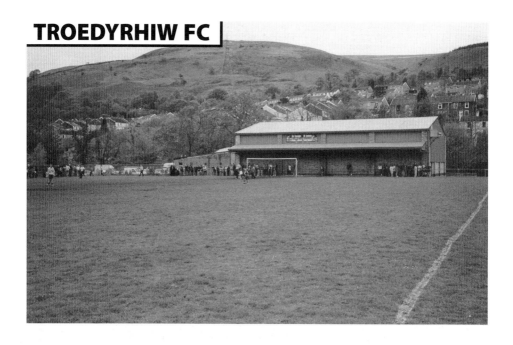

Founded: Early 1900s
Former Names: Troedyrhiw Stars FC
Nickname: 'Rhiw'
Ground: The Willows, Troedyrhiw, Merthyr Tydfil
Clubhouse Tel. Nº: (01443) 692198

Colours: Red and Black striped shirts, Black shorts
Correspondence: Roger Howells, 16 South View, Troedyrhiw, Merthyr Tydfil   CF48 4JA
Contact Tel. Nº: (01443) 693857
Fax Number: None

GENERAL INFORMATION

Social Club Telephone Nº: (01443) 692198
Club Shop: None
Car Parking: 50 spaces available at the ground
Coach Parking: At the ground
Nearest Railway Station: Troedyrhiw (200 yards)
Nearest Bus Station: Troedyrhiw (75 yards)
Nearest Police Station: Troedyrhiw
Police Telephone Nº: (01443) 690805

GROUND INFORMATION

Ground Capacity: 1,000
Seating Capacity: None
Record Attendance: Approximately 425
Pitch Size: 100 x 64 yards

ADMISSION INFO (2005/2006 PRICES)

Adult Standing: £2.00
Senior Citizen Standing: £1.50
Child Standing: 50p
Programme Price: Included with admission price

DISABLED SUPPORTERS INFORMATION

Wheelchairs: Accommodated
Disabled Toilets: Available at the Willows Community Centre next to the changing rooms
Contact Number: (01443) 691961

Travelling Supporters' Information:
Routes: Take the A470 towards Merthyr Tydfil then the B4054 to Troedyrhiw. The ground is situated between the River Taff and the railway line, opposite the Police Station.

AFC PORTH

Founded: 1950
Former Names: Beatus United FC and AFC Rhondda
Nickname: 'Black Dragons'
Ground: Dinas Park, Dinas, Porth, Rhondda, Mid Glamorgan
Ground Telephone Nº: (07890) 294842

Colours: Maroon & Blue shirts with Blue shorts
Correspondence: Eric Thomas, 28 Trealaw Road, Tonypandy, Rhondda   CF40 2NS
Contact Telephone Nº: (01443) 442395

GENERAL INFORMATION
Social Club Telephone Nº: (01443) 682329
Club Shop: Yes
Car Parking: At the ground
Coach Parking: At the ground
Nearest Railway Station: Dinas
Nearest Bus Station: Dinas
Nearest Police Station: Porth
Police Telephone Nº: –

GROUND INFORMATION
Ground Capacity: 2,000
Seating Capacity: 200
Record Attendance: 1,700
Pitch Size: 110 x 83 yards

ADMISSION INFO (2005/2006 PRICES)
Adult Standing: £2.00
Adult Seating: £2.00
Child Standing: 50p
Child Seating: 50p
Concessionary Standing: 50p
Concessionary Seating: 50p
Programme Price: Included with admission

DISABLED SUPPORTERS INFORMATION
Wheelchairs: Accommodated
Disabled Toilets: Available
Contact Number: (01443) 682329

Travelling Supporters' Information:
Routes: Exit the M4 at Junction 32 and take the A470 towards Merthyr Tydfil. Leave the A470 at signs for Pontypridd (Rhondda Valley). On reaching Porth follow signs for Dinas/Tonypandy and the ground is on the right after 3 miles.

BLAENRHONDDA AFC

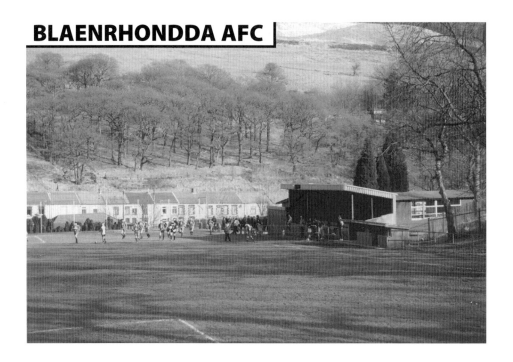

Founded: 1934
Former Names: None
Nickname: None
Ground: Blaenrhondda Park, Blaenrhondda, Mid Glamorgan
Ground Tel. Nº: None

Colours: Blue shirts and shorts
Correspondence: Stephen A. Rumble, 85 Brynhyfryd Terrace, Ferndale, Rhondda, CF43 4HT
Contact Tel. Nº: (01443) 730141
Fax Number: None

GENERAL INFORMATION
Car Parking: £1.00 per car in the local School Yard
Coach Parking: In the local School Yard
Nearest Railway Station: Treherbert
Nearest Bus Station: Bus stop just outside the ground

GROUND INFORMATION
Ground Capacity: 1,000
Seating Capacity: None
Record Attendance: Approximately 1,000
Pitch Size: 105 x 78 yards

ADMISSION INFO (2005/2006 PRICES)
Adult Standing: £2.00
Child Standing: £1.00
Programme Price: Usually included with Adult admission

DISABLED SUPPORTERS INFORMATION
Wheelchairs: Accommodated
Disabled Toilets: None
Contact Number: (01443) 730141

Travelling Supporters' Information:
Routes: Take the A4061 to Treherbert and follow the road into Tynewydd then Blaenrhondda. The main road in Blaenrhondda is Brook Street and the entrance to the ground is directly opposite the Post Office (look for the Post Office sign on the wall).

CAMBRIAN & CLYDACH VALE BOYS & GIRLS CLUB FC

Founded: 1965
Former Names: Cambrian United FC
Nickname: 'The Sky Blues'
Ground: King George V New Field, Clydach Vale, near Tonypandy
Ground Telephone N°: None

Club Colours: Sky Blue shirts and shorts
Correspondence: Keith Jenkins, 8 Hill Street, Penygraig, Rhondda Cynon Taff CF40 1LT
Contact Telephone N°: (01443) 436277
Fax Number: (01443) 420900

GENERAL INFORMATION
Social Club Telephone N°: –
Club Shop: None
Car Parking: At the ground
Coach Parking: At the ground
Nearest Railway Station: Tonypandy (1 mile)
Nearest Bus Station: Tonypandy (½ mile)
Nearest Police Station: Tonypandy
Police Telephone N°: (01433) 437563

GROUND INFORMATION
Ground Capacity: 1,000
Seating Capacity: None
Record Attendance: New ground – no record set as yet!
Pitch Size: 110 x 70 yards

ADMISSION INFO (2005/2006 PRICES)
Adult Standing: £2.00
Child Standing: Free of charge
Concessionary Standing: £1.00
Programme Price: Included with admission

DISABLED SUPPORTERS INFORMATION
Wheelchairs: Accommodated
Disabled Toilets: Available
Contact Number: (01443) 436277

Web Site: www.ccvbgc.co.uk
E-mail: jenkinskeith@btconnect.com

Travelling Supporters' Information:
Routes: From All Parts: Take the M4, exit at Junction 32 and take the A470 towards Merthyr Tydfil. Leave the A470 at signs for Pontypridd (Rhondda Valley). On reaching Porth, follow signs for Dinas/Tonypandy and the ground is next to the council offices after about 3½ miles.

CHEPSTOW TOWN FC

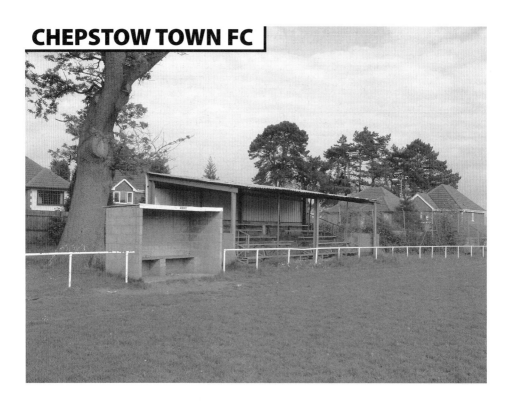

Founded: 1878
Former Names: None
Nickname: None
Ground: Newport Road, Chepstow
Ground Telephone Nº: (01291) 629220

Colours: Blue & White quartered shirts, Blue shorts
Correspondence: Mark Warby, 47 Green Street, Chepstow NP16 5BP
Contact Tel. Nº: (01291) 630798
Fax Number: None

GENERAL INFORMATION
Car Parking: At the ground
Coach Parking: At the ground
Nearest Railway Station: Chepstow (1 mile)
Nearest Bus Station: Chepstow (½ mile)
Nearest Police Station: Chepstow

GROUND INFORMATION
Ground Capacity: 1,000
Seating Capacity: 70
Record Attendance: Approximately 400
Pitch Size: 110 x 65 yards

ADMISSION INFO (2005/2006 PRICES)
Adult Standing: 50p (by programme)
Child Standing: Free of charge
Programme Price: Included with admission

DISABLED SUPPORTERS INFORMATION
Wheelchairs: Accommodated
Disabled Toilets: Available
Contact Number: (01291) 629731

Travelling Supporters' Information:
Routes: Exit the M48 at Junction 2, take the A466 towards Chepstow then turn right at the roundabout onto the A48. The ground is situated on the right after 300 yards opposite Chepstow Hotel.

CWMAMMAN UNITED AFC

Founded: 1976
Former Names: Glanamman FC
Nickname: None
Ground: Grenig Park, Cwmamman, Nr. Ammanford
Ground Tel. Nº: (01269) 823107
Web Site: www.cwmamman-afc.co.uk

Club Colours: Blue and Black shirts with Black shorts
Correspondence: Alun Rees, 81 Parc Brynrhos, Glanamman, Ammanford SA18 1JE
Contact Tel. Nº: (01269) 824364
Fax Number: (01269) 851096

GENERAL INFORMATION
Social Club Telephone Nº: (01269) 823107
Club Shop: None
Car Parking: Approximately 40 spaces at the ground
Coach Parking: Approximately 2 spaces at the ground
Nearest Railway Station: Neath (14 miles)
Nearest Bus Station: Ammanford (2½ miles)
Nearest Police Station: Ammanford
Police Telephone Nº: (01269) 592222

GROUND INFORMATION
Ground Capacity: 1,000
Seating Capacity: 150
Record Attendance: Approximately 250
Pitch Size: 99 x 69 yards

ADMISSION INFO (2005/2006 PRICES)
Adult Standing: £2.00
Child Standing: Free of charge
Programme Price: Included in the cost of admission

DISABLED SUPPORTERS INFORMATION
Wheelchairs: Accommodated
Disabled Toilets: Available
Contact Number: (01269) 824364

Travelling Supporters' Information:
Routes: Take the M4 then exit at the service area at Portabraham. Take the 2nd left heading for Ammanford (5 miles). On reaching Ammanford go straight through the lights towards Glanamman (3 mile). The ground is 1 mile after the Glanamman sign.

CWMBRAN CELTIC FC

Founded: 1925
Former Names: Cwmbran Catholics FC
Nickname: 'Celtic'
Ground: Cwmbran Stadium, Henllys Way, Cwmbran, Gwent
Ground Telephone Nº: (01633) 627100

Club Colours: Yellow shirts with Blue shorts
Correspondence: Malcolm Jarrett, 94 Marlborough Road, Greenmeadow, Cwmbran NP44 5EP
Contact Telephone Nº: (01633) 862689
Fax Number: None
E-mail: malcolm.jarrett@btinternet.com

GENERAL INFORMATION
Social Club Telephone Nº: (01633) 774019
Club Shop: None
Car Parking: At the ground
Coach Parking: At the ground
Nearest Railway Station: Cwmbran (2 miles)
Nearest Bus Station: Cwmbran (1 mile)
Nearest Police Station: Cwmbran (1 mile)
Police Telephone Nº: (01633) 838999

GROUND INFORMATION
Ground Capacity: 8,201
Seating Capacity: 3,000
Record Attendance: Not known
Pitch Size: 112 x 76 yards

ADMISSION INFO (2005/2006 PRICES)
Adult Standing: £2.00
Adult Seating: £2.00
Child Standing: Free of charge
Child Seating: Free of charge
Concessionary Standing: £2.00
Concessionary Seating: £2.00
Programme Price: Included with admission

DISABLED SUPPORTERS INFORMATION
Wheelchairs: Accommodated
Disabled Toilets: Available
Contact Number: (01633) 627100

Travelling Supporters' Information:
Routes: From All Parts: Take the M4, exit at Junction 26 and follow signs for Cwmbran. At the first roundabout (approximately 1½ to 2 miles) take the first exit. Proceed along Cwmbran Drive passing the Stadium on your right. At the next roundabout take the first exit and at the following roundabout take the 3rd exit. The Stadium entrance is 150 yards on the right.
On foot from the station – turn left out of the station car park and then right at the road junction towards the roundabout. Turn left at the roundabout and Henllys Way is on the right after approximately 1 mile.

GOYTRE FC (GWENT)

Founded: 1902
Former Names: None
Nickname: None
Ground: Plough Road, Penperlleni, Monmouthshire
Ground Tel. Nº: None

Colours: Red & Black striped shirts with Black shorts
Correspondence: David Melmoth, Carrig-y-Melin, School Lane, Penperlleni, Near Pontypool NP4 0AH
Contact Tel. Nº: (01873) 880569
Fax Number: None
Web site: www.goytrefc.co.uk

GENERAL INFORMATION
Car Parking: At the ground
Coach Parking: At the ground
Nearest Railway Station: Abergavenny (4 miles)
Nearest Bus Station: Abergavenny
Nearest Police Station: Pontypool

GROUND INFORMATION
Ground Capacity: 1,000
Seating Capacity: 50
Record Attendance: Approximately 400 vs Newport County
Pitch Size: 110 x 65 yards

ADMISSION INFO (2005/2006 PRICES)
Adult Standing: £2.00 (by programme)
Child Standing: £1.00 (by programme)
Under-14s: Free of charge
Programme Price: Included with admission)

DISABLED SUPPORTERS INFORMATION
Wheelchairs: Accommodated
Disabled Toilets: Available
Contact Number: (01873) 880569

Travelling Supporters' Information:
Routes: Exit the M4 at Junction 25A and take the A4042 to Pontypool. Continue past Pontypool towards Abergavenny and turn right into the village of Penperlleni by the Goytre Arms. Follow the road then turn first right after the railway bridge and the ground is situated about ½ mile along on the left.

LLANTWIT FARDRE FC

Founded: 1958
Former Names: Llantwit Fardre Juniors FC
Nickname: None
Ground: Tonteg Park, Llantwit Fardre, Pontypridd
Ground Telephone N°: None
Club Colours: Sky Blue shirts with Navy Blue shorts

Correspondence: Gary Lord, 7 Nightingale Gardens, St. Davids Manor, Church Village CF38 1GB
Contact Tel. N°: (01443) 204951
Fax Number: None
Web Site: www.llantwit-football.com
E-mail: chairlffcman@yahoo.com

GENERAL INFORMATION

Social Club Telephone N°: (01443) 207393
Car Parking: At the ground
Coach Parking: At the ground
Nearest Railway Station: Trefforest (2½ miles)
Nearest Bus Station: Pontypridd (4 miles)
Nearest Police Station: Church Village

GROUND INFORMATION

Ground Capacity: 1,000
Seating Capacity: None
Record Attendance: Approximately 300 (1972)
Pitch Size: 110 x 80 yards

ADMISSION INFO (2005/2006 PRICES)

Adult Standing: £2.00 (by programme)
Child Standing: Free of charge
Programme Price: Included with admission

DISABLED SUPPORTERS INFORMATION

Wheelchairs: Accommodated
Disabled Toilets: Available in nearby Community Centre
Contact Number: (01443) 671971

Travelling Supporters' Information:
Routes: Exit the M4 at Junction 32 and take the A470 towards Pontypridd. Take the exit at the North end of the Trefforest Industrial Estate, cross the River Taff and proceed up Power Station Hill to the traffic lights. Turn left onto the A473 and the ground is immediately on the left opposite CP Motors.

LLANWERN FC

Founded: 1963
Former Names: Spencer Works FC
Nickname: None
Ground: Newport Stadium, Spytty Park, Langland Way, Newport   NP19 4PT

Colours: Red shirts and shorts
Correspondence: Alan Watkins, 21 Traston Close, Newport   NP19 4TG
Contact Tel. Nº: (01633) 671748
Matchday Mobile Nº: (07762) 013310

GENERAL INFORMATION

Car Parking: Space for 500 cars at the ground
Coach Parking: At the ground
Nearest Railway Station: Newport
Nearest Bus Station: Newport
Police Telephone Nº: (01633) 244999

GROUND INFORMATION

Ground Capacity: 4,300
Seating Capacity: 1,200
Record Attendance: Approximately 100
Pitch Size: 112 x 72 yards

ADMISSION INFO (2005/2006 PRICES)

Adult Standing/Seating: £2.50 (by programme)
Child Standing/Seating: Free of charge
Programme Price: £2.50 (includes admission)

DISABLED SUPPORTERS INFORMATION

Wheelchairs: Accommodated
Disabled Toilets: Available
Contact: (01633) 671748

Travelling Supporters' Information:
Routes: Exit the M4 at Junction 24 and take the exit at the roundabout, signposted 'Southern Distributor Road'. Go straight on at the first two roundabouts then turn left at the 3rd roundabout. Carry straight on over the next two roundabouts, pass the Velodrome then turn left between the two Carcraft buildings. Take the 1st turning on the left into the Stadium car park.

NEWCASTLE EMLYN AFC

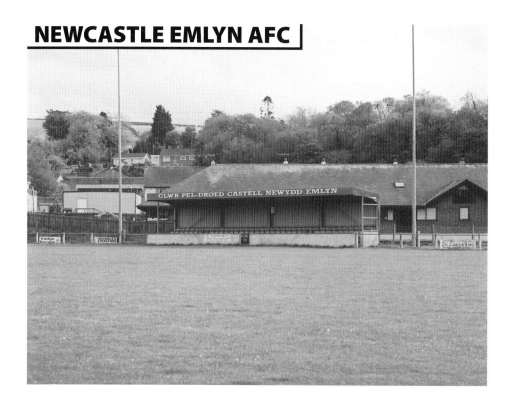

Founded: Before 1912
Former Names: None
Nickname: 'Emlyn'
Ground: Parc Emlyn, Newcastle Emlyn   SA38 9BE
Ground Tel. Nº: (01239) 710994
Web Site: www.newcastleemlynfc.com
E-mail: john@newcastleemlynfc.com

Club Colours: Red shirts and shorts
Correspondence: S. John O. Jones, 35 Blaenwern,
Newcastle Emlyn, Carmarthenshire   SA38 9BE
Contact Tel. Nº: (01239) 711200
Fax Number: (01239) 710803

GENERAL INFORMATION

Social Club Telephone Nº: (01239) 710007
Club Shop: Yes – at the Plough Hotel, Newcastle Emlyn
Car Parking: Adjacent to the ground
Coach Parking: Adjacent to the ground
Nearest Railway Station: Carmarthen (18 miles)
Nearest Bus Station: Newcastle Emlyn (200 yards)
Nearest Police Station: Newcastle Emlyn

GROUND INFORMATION

Ground Capacity: 2,000
Seating Capacity: 120
Record Attendance: 1,800 vs Chelsea (1991)
Pitch Size: 111 x 71 yards

ADMISSION INFO (2005/2006 PRICES)

Adult Standing: £2.00
Adult Seating: £2.00
Child Standing: 50p
Child Seating: 50p
Programme Price: £1.00

DISABLED SUPPORTERS INFORMATION

Wheelchairs: Accommodated
Disabled Toilets: Available nearby
Contact Number: (01239) 710994

Travelling Supporters' Information:
Routes: On reaching Newcastle Emlyn, travel through the outskirts of the town until you reach a junction near a Vauxhall Cawdor Garage. Turn right, travel 100 yards, passing the Plough Hotel by the zebra crossing until you reach the town square near the Central Cafe chip shop. Turn left, then drive straight on and turn into the cattle mart. At the bottom of the large car park, you'll see the ground.

PENRHIWFER FC

Founded: 1967
Former Names: None
Nickname: 'The Fer'
Ground: Penrhiwfer Park, Penrhiwfer, RCT.
Club Colours: Blue & Black shirts with Black shorts

Correspondence: Craig Williams, 2 Ashdale Road, Penrhiwfer, Rhondda Cynon Taff   CF40 1RT
Contact Tel. Nº: (0797) 367-6185
Web Site: None

GENERAL INFORMATION
Car Parking: At the ground
Coach Parking: At the ground
Nearest Railway Station: Tonypandy (3 miles)
Nearest Bus Station: Cardiff (15 miles)

GROUND INFORMATION
Ground Capacity: 1,000
Seating Capacity: None
Record Attendance: Not known
Pitch Size: 110 x 70 yards

ADMISSION INFO (2005/2006 PRICES)
Adult Standing: £2.00
Senior Citizen/Child Standing: £1.00
Programme Price: Included with admission charge

DISABLED SUPPORTERS INFORMATION
Wheelchairs: Accommodated
Helpers: Admitted
Prices: Normal prices apply
Disabled Toilets: None
Contact Number: (01443) 423108

Travelling Supporters' Information:
Routes: Exit the M4 at Junction 34 and take the A4119 (signposted Rhondda Valley). After about 5 miles pass Tonyrefail and turn left at the next roundabout signposted for Penrhiwfer. Continue up the hill across the mini-roundabout and take the 2nd turning on the left into Ashdale Road. The ground is situated on the right hand side.

PENTWYN DYNAMOS FC

Founded: 1975
Former Names: Pentwyn & Llanedeyrn Dynamos FC
Nickname: 'Dynamos'
Ground: Parc-y-Nant, Off Bryncelin Road, Pentwyn, Cardiff
Ground Tel. Nº: (029) 2054-9211

Colours: White shirts with Royal Blue shorts
Correspondence: Malcolm Fraser, 181 Glyn Eiddw, Pentwyn, Cardiff   CF23 7BT
Contact Tel. Nº: (029) 2073-2032
Fax Number: None

GENERAL INFORMATION
Car Parking: At the nearby Leisure Centre
Coach Parking: At the nearby Leisure Centre
Nearest Railway Station: Cardiff Central
Nearest Bus Station: Cardiff Central
Nearest Police Station: Canton
Police Telephone Nº: (029) 2022-2111

GROUND INFORMATION
Ground Capacity: 1,000
Seating Capacity: 50
Record Attendance: New ground so no record as yet
Pitch Size: 110 x 70 yards

ADMISSION INFO (2005/2006 PRICES)
Adult Standing: £2.00
Adult Seating: £2.00
Child Standing: £1.00
Child Seating: £1.00
Programme Price: Included with admission

DISABLED SUPPORTERS INFORMATION
Wheelchairs: Accommodated
Helpers: Admitted
Prices: Normal prices apply
Disabled Toilets: Available in the nearby Leisure Centre
Contact Number: (029) 2054-9211

Travelling Supporters' Information:
Routes: From the East: Exit the M4 at Junction 29 and take the A48. Take the 2nd exit signposted for Pentwyn and then take the 2nd exit at the roundabout into Bryncelin Road following signs for the Leisure Centre. The ground is on the left after 200 yards; From the West: Exit the M4 at Junction 30 and follow signs for Cardiff Gate. Turn right at the roundabout and continue along the dual carriageway. Continue in the right hand lane and turn right at the next roundabout onto the A48 which passes beneath. Turn off at the next junction signposted for Pentwyn, then as above.

RISCA UNITED AFC

Founded: 1946
Former Names: Risca and Gelli United AFC
Nickname: 'The Cuckoos'
Ground: Ty-Isaf Park, Isaf Road, Pontymister, Risca
Ground Tel. Nº: (01633) 615081

Colours: Black and White striped shirts, Black shorts
Correspondence: Stuart Luckwell, 37 Snowdon Close, Ty-Melin, Risca, Caerphilly NP11 6JF
Contact Tel. Nº: (01633) 615314
Fax Number: (01633) 615314

GENERAL INFORMATION

Club Shop: At the ground – during matches only
Car Parking: Limited number of spaces at the ground – larger car parks available nearby
Coach Parking: One space available at the ground
Nearest Railway Station: Newport (7 miles)
Nearest Bus Station: Newport (7 miles)
Nearest Police Station: Risca (¾ mile)
Police Telephone Nº: (01633) 612391

GROUND INFORMATION

Ground Capacity: 2,000
Seating Capacity: None
Record Attendance: Approximately 2,000
Pitch Size: 100 x 74 yards

ADMISSION INFO (2005/2006 PRICES)

Adult Standing: £2.00
Child Standing: £1.00
Programme Price: Included with admission price

DISABLED SUPPORTERS INFORMATION

Wheelchairs: Accommodated
Disabled Toilets: None
Contact Number: (01633) 615314

Travelling Supporters' Information:
Routes: From the South, East & West: Exit the M4 at Junction 28 and follow the A467 for approximately 5 miles. Exit the A467 at the roundabout signposted for Risca then go straight on at the mini-roundabout into Mill Street. Take the second right for Isaf Road and the ground; From the North: Head for Newport down the Sirhowy or Ebbw Valley from Tredegar, Blackwood and Ebbw Vale. At Crosskeys take the A467 South towards Newport then leave at the roundabout signposted Risca. Then as above.

SEVEN SISTERS AFC

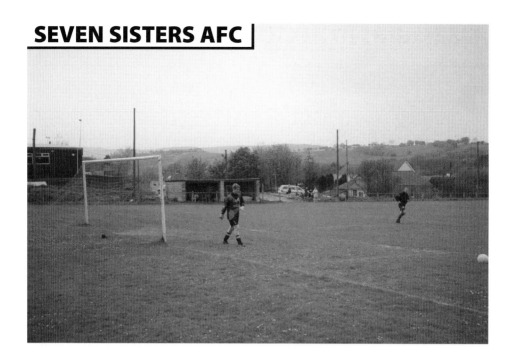

Founded: 1946
Former Names: None
Nickname: None
Ground: Welfare Ground, Church Road, Seven Sisters, Neath, West Glamorgan
Ground Tel. Nº: (01639) 700354

Club Colours: Green shirts and shorts
Correspondence: David Herdman, 79 Main Road, Duffryn Cellwen, Neath   SA10 9LA
Contact Tel. Nº: (01639) 700202
Fax Number: None

GENERAL INFORMATION
Club Shop: None
Car Parking: At the ground
Coach Parking: At the ground
Nearest Railway Station: Neath
Nearest Bus Station: Neath
Nearest Police Station: Neath

GROUND INFORMATION
Ground Capacity: 1,000
Seating Capacity: None
Record Attendance: Approximately 500
Pitch Size: 100 x 65 yards

ADMISSION INFO (2005/2006 PRICES)
Adult Standing: £2.00
Child Standing: Free of charge
Programme Price: £2.00 (includes admission)

DISABLED SUPPORTERS INFORMATION
Wheelchairs: Accommodated
Disabled Toilets: Available
Contact Number: (01639) 700202

Travelling Supporters' Information:
Routes: Exit the M4 at Junction 43 and take the A465 towards Merthyr Tydfil. Turn onto the A4109 Aberdulais and Seven Sisters is about 6 miles along this road. The Welfare Ground is on the right just before you reach the town.

TREHARRIS ATHLETIC FC

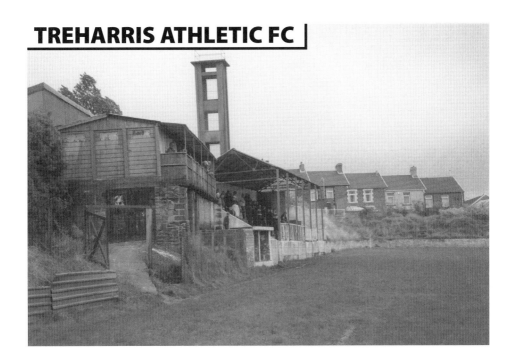

Founded: 1889
Former Names: None
Nickname: 'The Lilywhites'
Ground: Athletic Ground, Commercial Terrace, Treharris, Mid Glamorgan
Ground Tel. Nº: (07867) 600410 (Matchdays only)

Colours: Green and Yellow shirts with Green shorts
Correspondence: Mike Casey, 10 Windsor Road, Edwardsville, Treharris   CF46 5NP
Contact Tel. Nº: (01443) 411153
Fax Number: None

GENERAL INFORMATION
Club Shop: None
Car Parking: Limited number of spaces at the ground
Coach Parking: None
Nearest Railway Station: Quakers Yard (1 mile)
Nearest Bus Station: Treharris Square (500 yards)
Nearest Police Station: Treharris
Police Telephone Nº: (01443) 412455

GROUND INFORMATION
Ground Capacity: 1,000
Seating Capacity: None
Record Attendance: Not known
Pitch Size: 105 x 60 yards

ADMISSION INFO (2005/2006 PRICES)
Adult Standing: £2.00
Child Standing: £1.00
Programme Price: Included in admission price

DISABLED SUPPORTERS INFORMATION
Wheelchairs: Accommodated
Disabled Toilets: None
Contact Number: (01443) 411153

Travelling Supporters' Information:
Routes: Take the A470 from Cardiff or Merthyr and follow signs for Treharris. Once in Treharris, the ground is situated by the Fire Station.

TREOWEN STARS FC

Founded: 1926
Former Names: None
Nickname: 'Stars'
Ground: Bush Park, Uplands, Newbridge, Gwent
Ground Telephone Nº: (01495) 248249

Colours: Blue and White striped shirts, Black shorts
Correspondence: B. Huish, 9 Tredomen Terrace, Ystrad Menach, Hengoed   CF82 7BW
Contact Telephone Nº: (01443) 813628
Fax Number: None

GENERAL INFORMATION
Club Shop: None
Car Parking: At the ground
Coach Parking: At the ground
Nearest Railway Station: Pontypool
Nearest Bus Station: Newbridge
Nearest Police Station: Newbridge
Police Telephone Nº: –

GROUND INFORMATION
Ground Capacity: 700
Seating Capacity: None
Record Attendance: Not known
Pitch Size: 110 x 72 yards

ADMISSION INFO (2005/2006 PRICES)
Adult Standing: £2.00 (by programme)
Child Standing: £1.00 (by programme)
Concessionary Standing: £1.00 (by programme)
Programme Price: Included with admission

DISABLED SUPPORTERS INFORMATION
Wheelchairs: Accommodated
Disabled Toilets: None
Contact Number: (01495) 248249

Travelling Supporters' Information:
Routes: Take the A467 to Newbridge Town Centre and then follow the road to the Homeleigh Estate. Bush Park is situated in the Uplands area.

WEST END FC

```
No Ground Photograph was available
at the time of going to press
```

Founded: 1964
Former Names: None
Nickname: 'The End'
Ground: Pri Deri Park, Mayhill, Swansea
Ground Telephone Nº: None

Club Colours: Blue shirts and shorts
Correspondence: Dave Owens, 61 Gwynfor Road, Cockett, Swansea SA2 0XE
Contact Nº: (01792) 416161
Fax Number: None

GENERAL INFORMATION
Club Shop: None
Car Parking: At the ground
Coach Parking: Street Parking
Nearest Railway Station: Swansea Central (2½ miles)
Nearest Bus Station: Swansea Quadrant (3 miles)

GROUND INFORMATION
Ground Capacity: 1,000
Seating Capacity: 60
Record Attendance: Not known
Pitch Size: 110 x 72 yards

ADMISSION INFO (2005/2006 PRICES)
Adult Standing/Seating: £2.00
Child/Senior Citizen Standing/Seating: £1.00
Programme Price: Included with admission charge

DISABLED SUPPORTERS INFORMATION
Wheelchairs: Accommodated
Helpers: Admitted
Prices: Normal prices apply
Disabled Toilets: Available
Contact Number: (01792) 416161

Travelling Supporters' Information:
Routes: Exit the M4 at Junction 42 and take the A483 (Fabian Way) into Swansea. Go past Sainsbury's Supermarket on the left after about 6 miles, turn off right into Wind Street and follow the road to the T-junction. Turn left at the traffic lights onto College Street, move into the outside lane and take the 2nd exit at the roundabout into Belle Vue Way. Turn right at the traffic lights at the bottom of the hill, follow the road up the hill and take the last turning on the right into Eigen Crescent. The ground is approximately 500 yards along this road.

YSTRADGYNLAIS FC

Founded: 1910
Former Names: Gough Institute FC
Nickname: None
Ground: Recreation Ground, Ystradgynlais, Swansea
Ground Telephone N°: None

Club Colours: Graphite Blue shirts and shorts
Correspondence: Kevin Davies, 3 Pelican Street, Ystradgynlais SA9 1LG
Contact N°: (01639) 842523
Fax Number: None

GENERAL INFORMATION

Club Shop: None
Car Parking: At the ground
Coach Parking: At the ground
Nearest Railway Station: Neath (11 miles)
Nearest Bus Station: Neath (11 miles)

GROUND INFORMATION

Ground Capacity: 1,000
Seating Capacity: None
Record Attendance: Approximately 150
Pitch Size: 110 x 70 yards

ADMISSION INFO (2005/2006 PRICES)

Adult Standing: £2.00
Child/Senior Citizen Standing: £1.00
Programme Price: Included with admission charge

DISABLED SUPPORTERS INFORMATION

Wheelchairs: Accommodated
Helpers: Admitted
Prices: Normal prices apply
Disabled Toilets: Available
Contact Number: (01639) 842523

Travelling Supporters' Information:
Routes: Exit the M4 at Junction 45 and take the A467 to Ystradgynlais (approximately 12 miles). Upon reaching Ystradgynlais take the 2nd exit on the right off the A4067 towards the Industrial Estate and the ground is situated on the right hand side after 300 yards.

WALES INTERNATIONAL LINE-UPS AND STATISTICS 2004-2005

18th August 2004
v LATVIA *Riga*
P. Jones	Wolves (sub. M. Crossley 46)
M. Delaney	Aston Villa
A. Melville	West Ham United (sub. J. Collins 24)
R. Page	Cardiff City
B. Thatcher	Manchester City
R. Savage	Birmingham C. (sub. A. Johnson 46)
M. Pembridge	Fulham (sub. G. Roberts 69)
G. Speed	Bolton Wanderers
J. Koumas	West Brom. (sub. C. Robinson 90)
J. Hartson	Celtic (sub. G. Taylor 86)
C. Bellamy	Newcastle United

Result 2-0   Hartson, Bellamy

4th September 2004
v AZERBAIJAN (WCQ) *Baku*
P. Jones	Wolverhampton Wanderers
M. Delaney	Aston Villa
A. Melville	West Ham United
R. Page	Cardiff City
D. Gabbidon	Cardiff City
J. Koumas	West Brom. (sub. R. Earnshaw 88)
R. Savage	Birmingham City
G. Speed	Bolton Wanderers
M. Pembridge	Fulham (sub. J. Oster 45)
C. Bellamy	Newcastle United
J. Hartson	Celtic

Result 1-1   Speed

8th September 2004
v NORTHERN IRELAND (WCQ)
Millennium Stadium, Cardiff
P. Jones	Wolverhampton Wanderers
M. Delaney	Aston Villa (sub. R. Earnshaw 26)
J. Collins	Cardiff City
D. Gabbidon	Cardiff City
B. Thatcher	Manchester City (sub. P. Parry 63)
J. Oster	Sunderland
R. Savage	Birmingham City
G. Speed	Bolton Wanderers
J. Koumas	West Bromwich Albion
J. Hartson	Celtic
C. Bellamy	Newcastle United

Result 2-2   Hartson, Earnshaw

9th October 2004
v ENGLAND (WCQ)   *Manchester*
P. Jones	Wolverhampton Wanderers
S. Davies	Tottenham Hotspur
M. Delaney	Aston Villa
D. Gabbidon	Cardiff City
B. Thatcher	Manchester City
J. Koumas	West Brom. (sub. R. Earnshaw 73)
M. Pembridge	Fulham (sub. C. Robinson 59)
G. Speed	Bolton Wanderers
R. Giggs	Manchester United
C. Bellamy	Newcastle United
J. Hartson	Celtic

Result 0-2

13th October 2004
v POLAND (WCQ)
Millennium Stadium, Cardiff
P. Jones	Wolverhampton Wanderers
M. Delaney	Aston Villa
D. Gabbidon	Cardiff City
J. Collins	Cardiff City
B. Thatcher	Manchester City
S. Davies	Tottenham Hotspur
R. Savage	Birmingham City
J. Koumas	West Brom. (sub. P. Parry 86)
G. Speed	Bolton Wands. (sub. J. Hartson 79)
C. Bellamy	Newcastle United
R. Earnshaw	Cardiff City

Result 2-3   Earnshaw, Hartson

9th February 2005
v HUNGARY   *Millennium Stadium*
D. Coyne	Burnley
D. Gabbidon	Cardiff City
R. Page	Cardiff City
D. Partridge	Motherwell (sub. J. Collins 65)
R. Edwards	Wolves (sub. R. Weston 50)
C. Fletcher	West Ham United
S. Davies	Tottenham Hotspur
C. Robinson	Sunderland (sub. S. Roberts 90)
S. Ricketts	Swansea City
R. Earnshaw	West Brom. (sub. G. Roberts 75)
C. Bellamy	Newcastle United (on loan at Celtic)

Result 2-0   Bellamy 2

26th March 2005
v AUSTRIA (WCQ)
Millennium Stadium, Cardiff

D. Coyne	Burnley
M. Delaney	Aston Villa
R. Page	Coventry City
D. Gabbidon	Cardiff City
S. Ricketts	Swansea City
C. Fletcher	West Ham United
C. Robinson	Sunderland
S. Davies	Tottenham (sub. R. Earnshaw 75)
R. Giggs	Manchester United
C. Bellamy	Newcastle United (on loan at Celtic)
J. Hartson	Celtic

Result 0-2

30th March 2005
v AUSTRIA (WCQ)   *Vienna*

D. Coyne	Burnley
J. Collins	Cardiff City (sub. R. Page 58)
D. Gabbidon	Cardiff City
D. Partridge	Motherwell
M. Delaney	Aston Villa
S. Davies	Tottenham Hotspur
C. Fletcher	West Ham United
C. Robinson	Sunderland
S. Ricketts	Swansea City
C. Bellamy	Newcastle United (on loan at Celtic)
R. Giggs	Manchester United

Result 0-1

Welsh Premier League Fixtures 2005/2006 Season	Aberystwyth Town	Airbus UK	Bangor City	Caernarfon Town	Caersws FC	Cardiff Grange Quins	Carmarthen Town	Connah's Quay Nomads	Cwmbran Town	Haverfordwest County	Llanelli AFC	NEWI Cefn Druids	Newtown AFC	Port Talbot Town	Porthmadog FC	Rhyl FC	Total Network Solutions	Welshpool Town
Aberystwyth Town	■	17/12	18/03	24/09	18/11	30/08	31/03	03/12	14/04	09/09	17/02	07/01	03/02	29/10	26/12	20/01	03/03	14/10
Airbus UK	22/04	■	28/10	03/02	17/03	27/08	19/11	31/03	03/12	21/01	24/09	26/12	10/09	04/03	15/04	30/08	14/10	17/02
Bangor City	12/11	10/03	■	26/12	11/02	26/11	08/10	24/02	22/10	10/12	07/01	24/03	22/04	10/09	03/02	07/04	22/01	30/08
Caernarfon Town	11/02	17/09	02/01	■	27/08	25/02	14/01	07/09	28/01	12/03	01/04	07/10	12/11	17/12	18/11	21/10	14/04	03/12
Caersws FC	24/03	12/11	24/09	07/01	■	08/04	25/02	22/10	11/03	22/04	30/08	25/11	26/12	04/02	18/02	10/12	10/09	21/01
Cardiff Grange Quins	13/01	07/01	01/04	15/10	03/12	■	14/04	18/12	02/01	23/09	03/03	04/09	18/02	18/11	10/09	05/02	19/03	29/10
Carmarthen Town	25/11	25/03	18/02	04/09	15/10	10/12	■	11/03	12/11	26/12	20/01	08/04	07/01	24/09	04/03	22/04	03/02	10/09
Connah's Quay Nomads	08/04	25/11	17/10	20/01	04/03	22/04	29/10	■	25/03	07/01	10/09	09/12	30/08	18/02	17/03	26/12	23/09	03/02
Cwmbran Town	09/12	08/04	04/03	10/09	29/10	26/12	17/03	19/11	■	31/08	03/02	22/04	21/01	15/10	01/04	07/01	17/02	24/09
Haverfordwest County	27/01	04/09	15/04	29/10	17/12	10/02	02/01	27/08	13/01	■	17/03	17/09	04/03	02/12	15/10	08/10	31/03	19/11
Llanelli AFC	07/10	11/02	27/08	26/11	14/01	21/10	07/09	28/01	16/09	11/11	■	25/02	25/03	02/01	03/12	12/03	17/12	15/04
NEWI Cefn Druids	27/08	02/01	18/11	17/02	01/04	22/01	03/12	14/04	17/12	04/02	16/10	■	23/09	18/03	30/08	09/09	28/10	03/03
Newtown AFC	17/09	28/01	16/12	17/03	02/01	08/10	27/08	14/01	04/09	22/10	19/11	11/02	■	15/04	29/10	25/02	03/12	01/04
Port Talbot Town	10/03	22/10	28/01	22/04	17/09	25/03	11/02	08/10	24/02	08/04	26/12	12/11	10/12	■	21/01	26/11	30/08	27/08
Porthmadog FC	02/01	10/12	17/09	25/03	08/10	28/01	22/10	12/11	26/11	25/02	08/04	14/01	11/03	04/09	■	23/09	27/08	22/04
Rhyl FC	04/09	13/01	04/12	03/03	15/04	17/09	17/12	02/01	27/08	18/02	29/10	27/01	15/10	01/04	11/02	■	20/11	17/03
Total Network Solutions	23/01	26/02	04/09	11/12	29/01	13/11	18/09	10/02	09/10	27/11	22/04	12/03	07/04	14/01	07/01	26/03	■	02/01
Welshpool Town	24/02	07/10	13/01	08/04	04/09	11/03	28/01	16/09	11/02	25/03	10/12	21/10	26/11	07/01	17/12	11/11	26/12	■

Cymru Alliance 2005/2006 Fixtures	Bala Town	Bodedern	Buckley Town	Flint Town United	Glantraeth	Gresford Athletic	Guilsfield	Halkyn United	Holyhead Hotspur	Holywell Town	Lex XI	Llandudno	Llandyrnog United	Llanfairpwll	Llangefni Town	Penrhyncoch	Queen's Park	Ruthin Town
Bala Town		21/01	12/08	25/03	25/02	23/08	11/03	22/04	08/04	15/04	12/12	26/11	17/12	28/01	12/11	02/01	24/09	04/02
Bodedern	20/08		18/03	24/09	31/08	26/11	27/08	25/03	11/03	17/09	12/11	29/10	22/04	27/12	17/08	08/04	14/01	15/10
Buckley Town	29/10	04/02		08/04	01/04	13/09	05/11	02/01	22/04	27/08	24/08	12/12	21/01	24/09	26/11	17/08	22/10	11/10
Flint Town United	05/11	18/02	19/11		15/04	21/01	01/04	23/08	12/12	04/02	17/12	02/01	27/08	25/02	22/04	13/08	18/03	22/10
Glantraeth	15/10	02/01	12/11	26/11		25/03	29/10	28/01	24/08	22/04	18/02	14/01	08/04	17/08	12/12	11/03	17/09	20/08
Gresford Athletic	27/12	15/04	14/01	19/08	05/11		16/08	15/10	17/09	19/11	11/03	18/02	01/04	05/12	28/01	29/10	31/08	29/04
Guilsfield	22/10	28/01	25/03	12/11	18/03	17/12		12/12	26/11	21/01	02/01	22/04	13/08	04/02	08/04	24/08	15/10	24/09
Halkyn United	05/12	05/11	31/08	27/12	27/08	25/02	29/04		14/01	18/03	04/02	20/08	22/10	01/04	15/04	24/09	26/11	19/11
Holyhead Hotspur	19/11	22/10	05/12	29/04	27/12	04/02	15/04	13/08		25/02	21/01	17/08	24/09	18/03	31/08	27/08	01/04	05/11
Holywell Town	14/01	12/12	28/01	12/10	05/12	13/08	20/08	29/10	15/10		25/03	11/03	21/09	31/08	18/02	12/11	17/08	27/12
Lex XI	29/04	01/04	27/12	16/08	24/09	22/10	31/08	17/09	20/08	05/11		28/01	18/03	19/11	14/01	25/02	05/12	15/04
Llandudno	18/03	20/09	29/04	31/08	13/08	24/09	05/12	21/01	17/12	22/10	27/08		25/02	11/10	27/12	04/02	19/11	01/04
Llandyrnog United	17/08	05/12	20/08	28/01	19/11	12/11	14/01	11/03	18/02	26/11	29/10	15/10		29/04	17/09	25/03	27/12	31/08
Llanfairpwll	27/08	24/08	18/02	15/10	17/12	22/04	17/09	12/11	29/10	02/01	08/04	25/03	12/12		11/03	26/11	20/08	13/08
Llangefni Town	01/04	25/02	15/10	05/12	20/09	27/08	19/11	17/12	02/01	24/09	13/08	24/08	04/02	22/10		21/01	05/11	18/03
Penrhyncoch	31/08	19/11	17/12	14/01	22/10	18/03	27/12	18/02	28/01	01/04	15/10	11/02	05/11	15/04	20/08		29/04	05/12
Queen's Park	18/02	13/08	11/03	29/10	04/02	02/01	21/09	12/10	12/11	17/12	22/04	08/04	24/08	21/01	25/03	12/12		27/08
Ruthin Town	17/09	17/12	25/02	11/03	21/01	12/12	18/02	17/08	25/03	24/08	26/11	12/11	02/01	14/01	29/10	22/04	28/01	

Welsh Football

The independent voice of Welsh soccer

- *Unrivalled coverage of football in Wales*
- *Written by and for soccer enthusiasts*
- *published continuously for 12 years*
- *Eight issues per season (August – June)*
- *New format for 2005/2006 with colour photos*

**Annual subscription cost =
£23 (including 2 free back issues)**

Apply to: Welsh Football, 57 Thornhill Road, Cardiff, CF14 6PE

Every issue contains:

*Welsh Premier scene
Welsh League news
Cymru Alliance news
Pyramid round-up
Club features
National team comment
Up-to-the-minute
Statistics supplement*

Supporters' Guides Series

This top-selling series has been published annually since 1982 and contains 2004/2005 Season's results and tables, Directions, Photographs, Phone numbers, Parking information, Admission details, Disabled information and much more.

THE SUPPORTERS' GUIDE TO PREMIER & FOOTBALL LEAGUE CLUBS 2006

The 22nd edition featuring all Premiership and Football League clubs. *Price £6.99*

THE SUPPORTERS' GUIDE TO NON-LEAGUE FOOTBALL 2006

Following the reorganisation of Non-League Football this 14th edition covers all 66 Step 1 & Step 2 clubs – the Football Conference National, Conference North and Conference South.   *Price £6.99*

THE SUPPORTERS' GUIDE TO NON-LEAGUE FOOTBALL 2006 – STEP 3 CLUBS

Following the reorganisation of Non-League Football the 2nd edition of this book features the 66 clubs which feed into the Football Conference.   *Price £6.99*

THE SUPPORTERS' GUIDE TO SCOTTISH FOOTBALL 2006

The 14th edition featuring all Scottish Premier League, Scottish League and Highland League clubs.   *Price £6.99*

THE SUPPORTERS' GUIDE TO NORTHERN IRISH FOOTBALL 2006

Back after a long absence, this 3rd edition features all Irish Premier League and Irish Football League Clubs + results, tables & much more.   *Price £6.99*

THE SUPPORTERS' GUIDE TO EIRCOM FAI CLUBS 2005

Back after a long absence this 3rd edition features all Eircom League Premier and First Division Clubs + 10 years of results, tables & much more. *Price £6.99*

These books are available UK & Surface post free from –

Soccer Books Limited (Dept. SBL)
72 St. Peter's Avenue
Cleethorpes
N.E. Lincolnshire
DN35 8HU